never under the table

never under the table

the table

A story of
British Columbia's forests
and government mismanagement

joe garner

Cinnabar Press

Nanaimo, British Columbia

1991

Available at most book outlets
or order direct from:

CINNABAR PRESS
P.O. Box 392
Nanaimo, B.C., Canada V9R 5L3

Cover painting by Grace Smith

Published by
CINNABAR PRESS
P.O. Box 392
Nanaimo, B.C., Canada V9R 5L3

Designed and printed in Canada by
MORRISS PRINTING COMPANY LTD.
Victoria, British Columbia

*Dedicated to my daughter Joanne
and my indispensible assistant Joan Davis*

CONTENTS

Preface

Never Under the Table is a book about forests, loggers, multinational manufacturing complexes, Forest Management Licences (now Tree Farm Licences), sawmill operators big and small, truck loggers, the government of British Columbia's mismanagement, gyppos, and yours truly.

In 1922, brother Tom was 15 and I was 13 when we started truck-logging with a model-T Ford, a team of horses, a couple of cross-cut saws and a good peavey. We were dumping logs into Vesuvius Bay on the west side of Saltspring Island. This is when and where we learned that any tree with a dead top was usually rotten to the core. To the loggers they were "culls," something to get rid of without delay. These trees can be compared to our provincial governments from the early 1940s on into the late 1950s. You might wonder why.

Up until 1940, no one ever imagined that some day B.C. might be short of trees. In those days, when a valley was logged out, they just moved over the hill into the next. Then, in 1945, a Royal Commission recommended that there should be Forest Management Licences created to bolster the lumber and pulp industries. To qualify for a licence, applicants needed to be a Canadian company with $20 million and a manufacturing plant. These licence holders were supposed to replant sufficient trees to replace the volumes of timber they logged each year. In theory this sounded great, but the replanting was not properly done, or done at the absolute minimum required. Today, some 50 years later, we are running out of trees.

9

From the issuance of the first Forest Management Licence near Prince Rupert, there were rumours of contributions to government election funds. When the Social Credit party was elected in 1952, and Bob Sommers was appointed Minister of Lands and Forests, all hell broke loose. In my opinion, the heads of that government could well be compared to those dead-top trees. They were rotten from top to bottom and should have been removed from any further association with the forest. We are now at a critical point in the life of our forests, where major change is necessary if we are going to leave anything for our kids.

Research shows that B.C. has the potential to be the wealthiest forest producer in the world. We are far from it at present. After reading this book you will better understand why politics must be removed from the management of our forests.

I would like to thank Henry Castillou, a recently retired lawyer who also has a degree in forestry, for his untiring help. I extend my sincere thanks to Ron MacIsaac for advice and assistance with research and to all those who gave so willingly of their time and knowledge to help with the creation of this book. I would also like to express my appreciation to Barry Broadfoot and Maggie Paquet for editing and proofreading. Last, but by no means least, a special thank you to Dick Morriss and his capable staff for printing and arrangement.

JOE GARNER

CHAPTER ONE

Never Under the Table

Our head faller Bill Kelsey waved me down as I drove off the Denman Island Ferry with a pickup truck loaded with barrels of gas and diesel. He was dressed in a dark suit, white shirt and black tie, so I knew something was up. Loggers don't wear town clothes much in the woods.

"My brother was found dead on his work boat last night in Howe Sound, just north of Anvil Island," he said. "I'd like to have the rest of the week off to go and help with the funeral. My sister-in-law phoned last night and I've got to go over. She's in a bad state."

"I'm sorry. It must be a terrible shock. Don't worry about your job. Just go and do what you can. If I can be of help, please let me know."

Someone had spotted a boat going around in circles about a mile south of Bill's brother's logging camp in Howe Sound. His brother was found slumped over the steering wheel in the cabin.

There must have been a mouse problem, because also dead in the boat's cabin on the bunk were two grown cats. It had been cold and wet, and his brother had probably closed the door to stay warm. There was a leak in the exhaust system of the boat. That silent killer carbon monoxide had put Kelsey and the two cats to sleep, never to wake again.

When Bill returned, and was ready to finish cutting the rest of the timber, he said, "My sister-in-law wants me to help her sell the logging camp near Woodfibre at Foulger Creek. You interested? I have a map of the old timber still to be logged. Over nine million board feet around the Brennan Lakes, another ten million in the headwaters of Potlatch Creek."

That much timber was like waving a juicy steak in front of a hungry hunting dog. And pickings were getting lean by the fall of 1951.

"Yes, I'd like to have a good look at it," I told him. "Why don't we fly over and have a chat with your sister-in-law this weekend. Meet me early next Saturday morning at the dock on Quamichan Lake near Duncan. Say at eight."

We flew over, and the timber looked good and we agreed on a price. It was a fair deal and I wanted it done quickly. No point in waiting, as a bidding contest might start. The camp was ready to go, with two buildings. One was a cookhouse with a dining area and a private room for the cook. There was a good oil stove, dishes, pots, pans, and beds for a crew of ten loggers. The other was a bunkhouse with the bunks all made up—sheets, blankets, bedspreads and pillows. In a big cupboard near the wood heater were extra blankets and a complete change of flannelette sheets and pillow slips. Heavy duty wrenches, acetylene cutting and welding torches were in a lean-to, where there was even a little diesel electric generator to run the lights and fridge. A neat set-up.

Up in the timber was an older model D8 cat with a track arch, a diesel yarding donkey, some felled and bucked logs and a rigged spar tree ready to go. At the edge of a bluff up a bit from the camp was a Fordson donkey rigged to a gin pole and a floating stiff-leg down below for tightlining the logs into the saltchuck. You couldn't ask for a nicer small operation.

And yes, there was a good number of mice. I got a couple of barn cats from home in Duncan, put them in a cage, and flew them over in my Piper float plane on one of my first trips back after we'd closed the deal.

And no, the cats didn't get airsick. They fussed a bit during the takeoff from Quamichan Lake, then curled up in opposite corners of their cage and were fast asleep by the time we passed over Crofton.

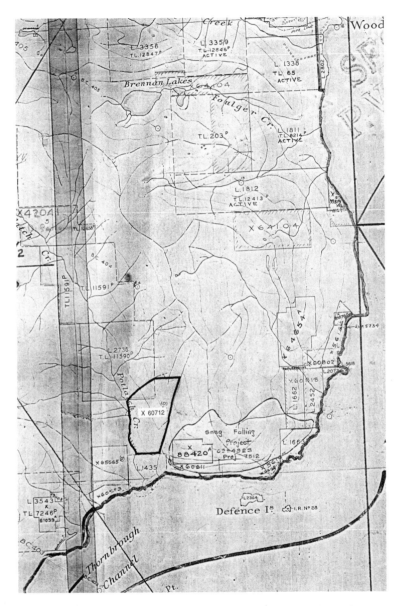

Map of Foulger and Potlatch Creeks in west Howe Sound area.

My next move was to see Jack Sexton, the manager of log supply for the H.R. MacMillan outfit, and he agreed to give the necessary financing for the right of first refusal on the logs.

Jack knew his stuff, and he made a suggestion regarding the drainage area of Potlatch Creek less than half a mile to the west of the Brennan Lakes and near the source of Foulger Creek.

"As you already know, there is a boys' summer camp on Lot 1435 right where Potlatch Creek runs into Howe Sound. Only last month I was asked to get a good logger to take down those big fir trees that are becoming dangerous to the buildings. I'm a director of this boys' camp and volunteered to take care of the job. We'd like to buy those logs when you have them in the water, boomed and ready for towing," Jack concluded with a grin. This was a bonus for me.

"Glad to move a machine and crew in early next year," I assured him. "No problem. Thanks."

"There is just one more little favour that could go along with the deal," he suggested. "If we paid you an extra couple of dollars per thousand because the logs are so close to our storage area, would you be willing to give half of that money back to the boys camp? The dining room and kitchen both need a new roof. The camp also needs more tables and benches and, of course, some extra dishes."

"You have a deal, Jack."

"You'll be logging on both Potlatch and Foulger Creeks," Sexton pointed out. "It looks to me like you should be in line to apply for a small Forest Management Licence on all that timber in both drainage areas."

"I'm ahead of you," and I laughed. "I've already looked that area over from the air and walked all through it. The timber is very good up at the higher levels. I've also talked to Bob Schultz of C.D. Shultz & Co. Ltd. I think they could do a good job on a proposal to our new government."

"They're about the best people in the province for such a job," Jack agreed. "And, I hear they have a 'real in' with our new Minister of Forests."

"Dave Bakewell is one of their best engineers," I replied. "He really does a fine job on road locations and logging layouts. I'll arrange to see both Bob Shultz and Dave first thing in the morning.".

"Good luck, Joe, and don't be afraid to ask if you think I can help." We shook on the deal, and I left with a thank you.

Logging layouts in steep country take time, and by now it was the autumn of 1952. Early in 1953, road plans, the required timber cruising, age data, timber descriptions and other information were all set out in a handsome brochure for submission to the office of Bob Sommers, the new Minister of Lands, Forests and Mines.

On Monday, August 31, 1953, Bob Schultz phoned, "Everything's ready to be submitted. All we need now is your final inspection and signature on the documents. Could you fly over to Horseshoe Bay tomorrow morning? Dave and I can be there by seven. It will take us the full day and maybe more to complete the inspection."

It was warm and clear next morning. I picked them up and at 7:15 we taxied up to the sandy beach in front of the boys' camp at Potlatch Creek. I made a deal with two of the older boys to look after my aircraft while we were up in the woods—"Ten dollars each if you do a good job," I offered.

Bob and I spent the next nine hours inspecting timber and following Dave Bakewell some five miles up the main roads he had surveyed to the top end of the valley. It was a fairly good grade with only one major bridge crossing the main creek about half-way up. There was big timber in the upper areas.

By 5:30 we were back at the beach, and the boys were happy to get their money. The Piper was licensed to carry the pilot and three passengers when wheel-equipped, but on floats, only two passengers were allowed. In large black letters on each side of the bright yellow tail assembly the registration letters CF-GTB showed up clearly. Apart from just looking good, it had saved us a lot of time and money in cruising timber and finding the best road locations in steep terrain. In ten minutes we had landed at Horse-shoe Bay, a 45-minute drive from downtown Vancouver.

"Be here tomorrow at the same time?" Bob asked, as he and Dave turned the plane so it faced out towards the open water. In those days, there were no giant B.C. Ferries or docking facilities, and only about one-tenth as many people. Horseshoe Bay was then only a village with one small government wharf.

Next morning Dave made some minor changes to the layout of the logging road, while Bob and I did more cruising and took borings to get the exact age of some of the bigger second growth trees. Some of those hemlock and balsam were over three feet through at chest height.

Bob, as a professional forester, was pleased and enthused with the prospect of his logging plan proposal being accepted. All the second growth was now more than 70 years old and ready for select harvesting or commercial thinning.

Bob asked me to fly Dave in the next day to check on the two old mining claims about a mile up from the beach, "Just to be sure."

"Dave, I'll pick you up at the seaplane dock at the Vancouver Airport. Eight o'clock. Need a bit of fuel to keep this thing in the air, you know," I added. Next morning Dave was there, and helped to service the plane. We were back by 4:00 p.m.

"Bob will phone you soon as he hears from Forestry," Dave said when I let him off at the Fraser River float plane dock.

On Wednesday morning, September 9, 1953, Bob called saying in an excited voice, "Better come over and sign the papers for the Foulger-Potlatch deal."

"I'll meet you at Horseshoe Bay in half an hour," I told him. "Bring your papers and maps so we can have one last look at the timber from the air. We can look at the whole area from about 5,000 feet up, then land and make a final logging appraisal of all that second-growth hemlock and balsam."

Bob didn't say much while we were walking up the old skid road and into the timber. I had brought along some sandwiches and a bottle of beer for each of us. After the inspection, we sat on

16

a couple of big old fir stumps. I opened the beer and handed Bob one with a cheese sandwich, saying, "Thought we should have something wet to celebrate with, seeing everything's O.K."

Bob ate slowly, drank the beer, and then said quietly, "This deal can be signed, sealed and delivered by noon tomorrow. But there's one little catch."

"Sounds good, but what's the little catch?" I asked.

Bob was silent for almost a full minute. He was nervous. Not like him, with his enthusiastic nature and good humour. "Some high official in our new government is demanding a payoff. He wants $20,000 before he signs. In small bills. Nothing over twenty. No questions asked. There is an agent in Vancouver to whom I'll give the money. This same agent also takes the contract to the government official for his signature, then returns it to me," and he looked away. So, there it was. Just like that.

Neither of us spoke another word until we had finished our lunch. Bob was still looking up at the trees when I got down from my stump and walked over to stand directly in front of him.

"If what you just said is true, you are asking me to be an accomplice to a bribery, and $20,000 is not what I consider a small bribe. Bob, this would make both of us accessories in this crime and we could find ourselves in jail for up to five years or more. I will never be a party to any such proposition."

Bob stood down from his stump, shrugged, and said, "You know, Joe, the big outfits that want Forest Management Licences all have to pay. It's one way or another. Either they donate large sums to the election funds, or they donate in some other fashion. There are ways."

"Who in hell would get the $20,000? Who's the guy, or guys?" I asked.

"Can't give you any names, Joe, but I can tell you it's divided up three ways."

"Bob, you just send in your bill for what's been done and it'll be paid. Let's get the hell out of here. Tell the people you're dealing with to put their money where it will do them the most good, and I'm not talking about some bank. Today this finishes

17

off any future business we might have enjoyed together. Been nice knowing you. No deal. Let's go."

After dropping Bob Schultz at Horseshoe Bay, I headed up Howe Sound and followed the railroad past Anderson and Seton Lakes on into Lillooet, then followed the Fraser River all the way to Quesnel—360 air miles northeast of Vancouver. My destination was Western Plywood's mill, where I set the Pacer down on the Fraser River south of Quesnel. Company manager Ian McQueen and I talked over Garner Bros. Ltd.'s contract for the following year to log on their long-term timber sale. Late that afternoon we signed the contract, then went out for a steak.

"There certainly is some skullduggery going on at the top level of the Forest Service, and we don't like it!" Ian said. I thought, "so I'm not the only one."

I nodded, and said, "That's the main reason we decided to log on your long-term timber sale south of town. I think you're dead on. We don't want anything more to do with Forest Management Licences." But I didn't tell him what I knew—that something was very wrong.

"The new tax on logging land that the government is proposing to put on all the old timber licences and leases is going to make it impossible to hold that land as a future timber supply," Ian said. "The whole system is being turned around."

"That tax was a major reason why we were applying for that small management licence," I explained to Ian. "Only management licence holders will be able to amalgamate those old timber licences and afford the tax because they will be able to write it off against their stumpage." (Stumpage is the price that the government charges for timber harvested).

We also discussed forest management in general, and the way things were being handled on their Forest Management Licence #5, north of Quesnel. Those old Forest Management Licences are now called Tree Farm Licences. The name was changed in the late 1950s after the Bob Sommers bribery trial, but who can say if any of the rules were ever really changed?

One man who questioned the rules was Gordon Gibson, a big-time gyppo logger on the West Coast of Vancouver Island. He felt that small loggers were reluctant to voice their opposition to a tax that was in the interests of the large companies for fear of losing their log markets. In defending the tax, Lands and Forests Minister Robert Sommers said the tax had nothing to do with the small logger because few of them held any timber leases.

"Of course they didn't," the tough and flamboyant Gibson declared. "They were already being squeezed out!"

Gibson, who later became a Member of the Legislative Assembly, also drew attention to what he called the disgraceful way in which the big companies were buying the rights to log the best areas in the Public Working Circles, further disenfranchising the independent loggers. It had been recommended by the Sloan Commission in 1945 that half the timber was to go to the big companies as Forest Management Licences, and half to the truck loggers—the independents—in the form of Public Working Circles. This was the first real attempt to manage B.C.'s forests to ensure a sustained yield.

When Gibson brought his concerns up with government, both Forest Minister Sommers and Premier William Andrew Cecil 'Wacky' Bennett told him to "mind his own business."

Gibson maintained the business of the province's forests was also the business of the taxpayers. He was becoming widely known as an outspoken critic of the government's forest licence granting policies. Aggressive and successful, Gordon Gibson commanded a great deal of media attention.

B.C.'s Chief Justice Gordon Sloan was appointed to hear submissions from both sides in the controversy. At first there was a good number representing the truck loggers—the small companies—but they dropped out one by one as time and markets ran out. Eventually Gibson seemed to be the only one speaking out for the small loggers, a vital part of B.C.'s number one industry. He was still continuing to argue loudly against some of the briefs presented by at least 10 highly-paid lawyers on behalf of their corporate clients, the forest giants. At the lengthy hearing,

Chief Justice Sloan ordered Gibson to sit down and be quiet. But he was so enraged by the unfairness of the situation he continued to speak, and win newspaper headlines.

When Sloan ordered Gibson out for contempt, the angry Gibson promised to get himself elected so he could appeal to the highest court: that of the people of the province.

Get elected he did. As Liberal MLA for Lillooet, he could now speak in the Legislature with all the privilege and protection of legislative immunity. And he talked with no holds barred.

When the Legislature was debating the Forests estimates, Forests Minister Sommers wasn't answering any questions. Having been ignored again and again, Gibson stood and shouted, "I firmly believe that money talks and that money has talked in this...Evidence will come out showing wrongdoings by this government..." Gibson referred specifically to his allegations that the government was not being open or above board in its method of granting Forest Management Licences. The newspapers began using the explosive phrase 'Money Talks' to describe the rapidly growing controversy—and the descriptive term stuck firmly in the public's mind.

Because he dared to speak out on February 16, 1955, Liberal MLA Gordon Gibson was expelled from the Legislature by the Social Credit Speaker of the House Tom Irwin for refusing to withdraw the comments he had made in the Legislature the previous day. This time he made B.C. history as the first MLA to be "named" by the Speaker, resulting in his expulsion—and the fight was really on! This was the news story of the year.

Gibson demanded that the whole issue should be referred to the House Standing Committee on Forestry for investigation by members of all four political parties in the province, thus ensuring fairness. The time bomb was ticking.

On February 17, 1955, Gibson phoned me, asking, "How'd you like to join me and my wife for dinner this evening?"

"What time and where?"

"The Empress Hotel, seven o'clock," he answered.

"Thanks, Gordon. I'll see you there."

That evening in Victoria, Gibson explained what he knew about the "big boys" paying someone to get management licence timber. He didn't know everything, but he knew enough.

If he needed more evidence, I could help him with some first-hand knowledge of my own, I told him.

"Thanks, Joe," he replied. "I don't think any more proof is needed at present. Hell, I'm getting telegrams and phone calls from all over the province urging me to hold my ground. They are all offering help if it's needed. As a matter of fact, I'm considering resigning my seat in the Legislature in order to force a by-election. Right now this seems to be the best way to show the government what a shoddy way they're managing our forests. It's completely criminal, in my opinion," Gordon concluded.

Gibson was reinstated in the Legislature by what was described as "a manoeuvre to allow the government to worm out of the charge with the least embarrassment." But after his "Money Talks" charge failed in court, he resigned and ran in a by-election on the issue. He lost.

Gibson said, "It cost the government millions of dollars to defeat me in that riding. Every Cabinet minister spent two weeks around Lillooet promising all kinds of goofy schemes that could never be carried out. Every baby within a radius of 25 miles had been kissed at both ends."

As much as the government tried to bury the case, it was not allowed to die. Government corruption was the theme, and the media had a field day. By now, there were other players at the table.

In December of 1955, Vancouver lawyer David Sturdy appeared before the Sloan Forestry Commission and stated that he had a "certain body of evidence showing that the Minister of Lands and Forests, Robert Sommers, had received considerations for the issuance of Forest Management Licences." When the commission refused to hear Sturdy's "body of evidence," Sommers launched a suit against him for libel and slander.

15

(Dept. of Lands & Forests — Forest Service — OCT 23 1957 — Victoria, B.C.)

Garner Bros. Ltd.,
Box 398,
Duncan, B. C.

Dear Sirs:

This will acknowledge receipt of your application of October 10th, 1957 for Crown Timber in the vicinity of Petlatch Creek.

An examination had been made previously of this area and it was determined that, although there are patches of mature timber in the area, removal of the mature timber would result in excessive damage to the surrounding immature stands.

We must advise, therefore, that your application is being disallowed at this time in the best public interest.

Yours truly,

D. B. Tayler,
District Forester.

c.c. Chief Forester - application attached

Typical refusal letter.

Sommers publicly denied allegations of bribery: "The past while has been the era of the great, great political smear...I challenge any Liberal to place a charge against me."

Two long and stormy name-calling years after the first allegations against Robert Sommers, preliminary court hearings started. This court case developed into one of the longest and most expensive legal trials ever to take place in Canadian history up to that time.

Sometimes I'm sorry I didn't blow the whistle on it all back in the fall of 1953. But I was 'small potatoes' and business activities were pressing—and the government was in total control.

George Whittaker bought our timber and camp equipment when we moved out of Foulger Creek and started logging in Quesnel, and my involvement with the Foulger Creek area was never resumed.

As the years have gone by, I've had plenty of time to think about that Howe Sound morning in September, 1953, the day Bob Schultz asked me to join in a bribery conspiracy by paying him $20,000. He would have guaranteed the Foulger-Potlatch Creek Tree Farm Licence contract—signed and approved by the next day. That was almost two years before Gordon Gibson stood in the Legislature and stated "Money Talks."

Because our company had refused to participate in the bribery scheme, we were apparently blacklisted by B.C. Forestry officials when it came to acquiring any future public timber. There always seemed to be some minor reason why our applications were not processed. One of the favorite reasons became almost standard and undebatable: "Your application for [so and so] timber is not in the best public interest," or words to that effect.

In the past, Garner Bros. Ltd. had logged numerous government timber sales with little or no problem in having our sales cleared and deposits returned. It was only after the Potlatch Creek episode and the $20,000 bribe demand that the previously open door to government timber was slammed in our face. From that time forward we had to either log on contract for the big Tree

Farm Licence owners or search out and buy timber from private land owners.

The word was out—and so were we.

The way it was in the 1940s. BCARS HP81035

CHAPTER TWO

Money Talks

My personal experience with bribery was small compared to some of the rumoured amounts being offered by the bigger companies. People in the B.C. lumber industry, particularly the independent loggers, had been voicing their concerns about practices surrounding the granting of Forest Management Licences for years, while the general public had been unaware of any wrong doings.

One of the first public indications came early in 1955, when Liberal MLA Gordon Gibson was expelled from the provincial Legislature for his comment: "I firmly believe that money talks and money has talked in this!" Gibson had made his comments during the debate on the Forests estimates. It was a direct accusation of the government's "mismanagement and favouritism in the awarding of Forest Management Licences."

Under the protection of parliamentary privilege, Gibson charged that both Robert E. Sommers, the Minister of Lands and Forests, and the Social Credit government itself were corrupt. He demanded that an investigation be done by the Legislature's Forestry committee, which had representation from all four political parties—Social Credit, the CCF which is now the NDP, the Conservatives and Liberals.

Such an uproar took place that Attorney-General Robert Bonner appointed Mr. Justice Arthur Lord of the Supreme Court to hold a one-man judicial inquiry into the allegations. When called before the commission, Gibson, unable to claim parliamentary immunity as he could in the Legislature, half-heartedly recanted, but promised he would somehow bring all the facts out into the open in the near future.

Only one other witness appeared before the Lord inquiry, and that was Deputy Minister C.D. Orchard, Bob Sommers' right-hand-man. In spite of objections by government forestry officials, Sommers and other Cabinet ministers wanted to approve B.C. Forest Products' application for a Clayoquot Forest Management Licence. Sommers had asked Orchard to 'doctor' the files so it would appear he had recommended approval of this licence. Orchard said he wouldn't go that far to help cover up the political bungling, but he assured Sommers he wouldn't blow the whistle either. As a result of Orchard's confusing testimony, the judge dismissed Gibson's charges as groundless. He concluded there had been no impropriety on the part of anyone in connection with the issuing of Forest Management Licences, which were vitally important, even absolutely necessary for the economic health of the major lumber company.

To get a better understanding of this episode and the story that follows, it helps to know that near the beginning of World War II, the Liberals and Conservatives of British Columbia had formed a coalition government to prevent the increasingly popular CCF from being elected.

Right after the war, this coalition government began issuing Forest Management Licences as recommended by the first Sloan Commission in December 1945. This was an entirely new system of granting harvesting rights in public forests.

Previously, most of the public timber was staked out by inde-pendent logging companies. The Forestry Department would ap-prove the sale and declare the lowest price they would accept, known as the "upset price." This sale would then be advertised and sold by public auction to the highest bidder. There were few government regulations in how harvesting would be carried out. It was usually mandatory to burn the slash to prevent forest fires, but no replanting was required.

Now, because of the Sloan Commission, the government was offering to issue cutting rights to huge blocks of timber known as

Forest Management Licences. The companies applying for the huge timber areas had to have, or guarantee to build, manufacturing plants to process the logs either into pulp or lumber. The companies also had to have sufficient funds to replant all logged areas. These conditions meant that only the large companies could qualify. This was the beginning of the province's reforestation policy on a proposed sustained yield basis.

The first Forest Management Licence was FML #0, and was issued to the Vancouver Water District. It was small, not worthwhile to the large companies, and allowed selective logging.

The second, granted in 1948, was FML #1, over the massive Skeena River and Nass River watersheds. By 1952, when the Social Credit Party formed the government, nine Forest Management Licences had been issued, or were in the process of being issued, covering millions of acres of virgin forest.

Because of these new regulations, the small logging companies and the independent sawmills were being squeezed out by big capital. Gordon Gibson openly accused the Socred government, and especially the Forestry Department, of not looking at anyone worth less than $20 million. It was rumoured that if a company wanted a management licence they had to contribute generously to the campaign funds of the government in power. With this licence system, there was great potential for corruption and the elimination of the gyppo logger—the small, often family-run operation.

In order to look more equitable, the government created Public Working Circles, which were supposed to be reserved for the independent loggers, often members of the Truck Loggers Association. One of the hotspots was the Clayoquot Public Working Circle on the west coast of Vancouver Island. B.C. Forest Products Ltd. had applied for a management licence over a large portion of the Clayoquot Public Working Circle, and was courting government officials and Bob Sommers.

E.P. Taylor, head of the huge Toronto-based Argus Corporation, met with Premier Bennett, Sommers, Attorney-General Bonner and others in an attempt to secure this licence.

Soon rumours began to circulate. Taylor had received not only an assurance he would get the huge money-making licence he wanted, but also his B.C. Forest Products would get a bonus patch of forest already set aside for the local loggers. This "patch" was practically all of the Clayoquot Public Working Circle. As a logger, Gordon Gibson was speaking out in defence of the independents, whose livlihood and future depended upon access and a fair share of this timber. It became a classic case of David and Goliath. The little logger Gibson had pitted himself against a government giant in the person of Robert Edward Sommers, Minister of Lands, Forests and Mines.

Sommers was born January 3, 1911, and had been a youth leader, a member of the Royal Canadian Legion band, the Kiwanis Club, the Parent-Teacher Association, conductor of the Castlegar Kiwanis Male Voice Choir, a member of the Knights of Pythias (K.P. Lodge) and the Trail City Club. He was also an accomplished trumpet and violin player and leader of his own orchestra.

This upstanding citizen had successfully run for Social Credit in his Rossland-Trail riding. In those days, MLAs didn't earn much money, and certainly not enough to maintain a lavish lifestyle. To many, Sommers appeared to be broke from the day he landed in Victoria. It was well known Sommers had a few bad habits, notably drinking and gambling, that could erode the income he received as a member of the Cabinet. That was the talk of the loggers in the Vancouver Forest District.

It was also rumoured that Sommers borrowed considerable amounts of money in an effort to sustain these habits from H. Wilson "Wick" Gray, the owner of two limited companies, Pacific Coast Services Ltd. and Evergreen Lumber Sales Ltd. It was frequently insinuated that for the right sum of money, Gray could guarantee anyone a Forest Management Licence because he had Sommers in his pocket.

These rumours helped to set the stage for Gibson's accusations in the Legislature. But he got no satisfaction from government.

Meanwhile, the Opposition continued to hammer away at Sommers in the House, with no success. The government ministers erected a wall of silence and the public had very little knowledge of what actually lay behind Gibson's charges. It was to be several years before any of the truth came out, but the Vancouver and Victoria papers kept up a drumbeat of criticism.

Rumours began to break through the silence after an article appeared in the Vancouver newspapers on May 27, 1958. It reported allegations that B.C.'s Lands and Forests Minister, Robert Sommers, "...was going to receive $48,960 as his share of a three-way split of bribe money up to November, 1954..."

Eventually, the Crown was forced to lay charges.

Explaining to the jury in what was then Canada's longest criminal trial and the first-ever to convict an elected minister of the Crown, Charles Eversfield, an accountant with the logging firm Pacific Coast Services Ltd., told the court that "...the matter was becoming so involved he had to keep 'a running summary' on how the money was split."

Eversfield was a prime witness in the case against Lands and Forests Minister Robert Sommers, Pacific Coast Services Ltd. and its President, H. Wilson Gray, plus a number of other forestry companies and individuals.

The story is long and messy, and so besmirched the reputations of both B.C.'s Forests ministry and some large logging companies that vestiges of it still linger to this day.

On November 6, 1958, the *Province* newspaper reported how Vancouver lawyer David Sturdy had "started the ponderous wheels of justice turning in the Sommers case almost three years earlier."

It had begun in late September, 1955, when an accountant named C.W. Eversfield came into Sturdy's office. (Sturdy had known Eversfield for some 20 years, but he hadn't done any business with him during the five years Eversfield had worked for Gray's Pacific Coast Services Ltd.) The accountant's story of payoffs to Sommers contained a complete rundown of names, places and amounts. This shook the lawyer Sturdy up considerably. After that meeting, Eversfield carried out his original plan to leave the company and move to California.

The impact of Eversfield's accusations hit Sturdy full force. He began gathering other information and evidence to substantiate the charges. He even went down to California to interview Eversfield again, to obtain his statutory declaration and to collect any further documentation he would need.

Armed with this "body of evidence," Sturdy appeared before Attorney-General Bonner on December 7, 1955. Sturdy presented Bonner with documents in which Eversfield swore under oath that "as accountant for Pacific Coast Services Ltd., he had knowledge of 10 separate payments made to Sommers, totalling $13,609." This sworn statement, later to be used in court, listed the dates for the transactions and traced the source of the funds and their method of payment. Other sums were listed as being "earmarked for Sommers and yet to be paid in some manner."

The following day, Sturdy received this telegram from Bonner, who was a friend of Sommers':

> Had no prior knowledge of purpose of your visit yesterday but anonymous phone call to expect attack upon a government minister made sense by time you left (Stop).
>
> Your mysterious behaviour including refusal to discuss subject matter of interview in arranging appointment, desire to conceal whereabouts of your informant, your advice that informant had in hand or at hand material supposedly supporting allegations made for two years but not presented to the Lord commission, and that you were advised of such material as long ago as September, together with contents of today's wire, all now coinciding with a by-election campaign in Vancouver Centre, fills me with profound skepticism toward entire matter (Stop).
>
> Particularly in view of minister's reaction thereto (Stop).
>
> In circumstances your unsupported document and your suggestion of criminal conspiracy or activity by directors and management of seven companies seem far-fetched.
>
> (signed) R.W. Bonner

Angered by the wire, and financed in part by lumberman Gibson, as it later was disclosed, Sturdy decided to "fight this through." Bonner's telegram had set out five reasons given by the minister for not taking action. The sixth reason was stated in the Legislature on January 31, 1956, when Bonner said he had "not been given a body of evidence."

In the court case, Sturdy countered, "That's not true. I had some 200 documents with me in a suitcase. I showed them to him." Sturdy even said he had offered to bring in a police constable to verify the contents of his briefcase.

The seventh reason occurred by way of the by-election in the late summer of 1956 in the Vancouver Centre riding when Bonner said the "whole thing was a conspiracy to wreck forest management."

When Sturdy asked Bonner whether the so-called anonymous person referred to in the telegram was a lawyer, Bonner said no, to which Sturdy asked, "Now, how could the Attorney-General know he wasn't a lawyer when the man was supposed to be anonymous?"

A clean shot!

Sturdy's continued desire to pursue his expensive cause was motivated, as he told a reporter, "by downright indignation at the possibility of an important Cabinet post being liable to bribery."

In November, 1976, 18 years later, the *Vancouver Sun* reported on the background of this case by reprinting an article originally appearing November 14, 1958. That article was written by the late Jack Brooks who had covered the infamous trial from start to finish. Brooks reported what had happened in the long interval between the first allegation and the first court hearing:

> ... when lawyer David Sturdy ... walked into Attorney-General Robert Bonner's office with his body of evidence ... Bonner was 'skeptical.' He thought the allegations 'far-fetched ... particularly in view of the minister involved.'
>
> When they were gone, according to Sommers' testimony at the trial, Bonner acted secretly. He called in Sommers and told him to 'get back the notes' the promissory notes he had given H.W. Gray for his 'loans.' Bonner helped him to ... draw up the necessary legal papers to make sure they were in proper legal phraseology.

The first public information on the allegations came December 16, when Sturdy walked into the Vancouver courthouse to show his 'evidence' to then Chief Justice Gordon Sloan, sitting in the Forestry commission.

Judge Sloan refused to hear Sturdy's evidence, saying such "allegations were not in his terms of reference." When Sommers was confronted by reporters about the allegations, he quickly denied them and, three days later, initiated proceedings to sue Sturdy for both slander and libel. The case dragged on for nearly two years, and Sturdy won by default when Sommers failed to appear in court.

Watchdog-lawyer Sturdy said a rumour had gone around that he had been well paid for his actions in bringing his investigations and disclosure to public notice and his continuing pursuit of the allegations of bribery.

"As a matter of fact, if it were not for my partners, I would be a ruined man. For two years I did nothing but work on this case or worry about it. I didn't handle one single major lawsuit in my practice."

Sturdy said that after his early talks with chief Crown witness Charles Eversfield, he approached 'Money Talks' Gibson and made a deal that he "put up funds which are reasonably necessary to bring the case before some kind of judicial body." Gibson was to supply the funds, but Sturdy was to remain in control of the case. Behind-the-scenes work on the Sommers case was financed with $4,950 and he had repaid $1,000 of that. The money was spent on trips to Los Angeles to see Eversfield, out-of-pocket expenses, a trip to Ottawa to the Supreme Court of Canada, and in direct payments to Eversfield who needed it. Sturdy did not personally benefit. The funds went towards seeing that justice was done.

In the meantime, however, the slow-moving slander and libel case had effectively silenced any possible political repercussions. This legal manoeuvre had bought the Social Credit government time at very little cost. When the opposition parties got hold of the information, they "tore into Bonner," as Brooks wrote, saying either the Lands and Forests Minister had accepted bribes or the accusers were perjurers, and "either way he should act," and "not abdicate his responsibility" as the province's Attorney-General. Premier Bennett shouted across the legislative floor "propaganda! propaganda!" a word he was going to use scores of times in the next two years.

Bonner continued to defend his inaction in investigating the bribery allegations against Sommers, "claiming he had never seen the body of evidence," and even went so far as to declare that he had tried to have another meeting with Sturdy, but had failed.

Then, in Brooks' article, it "leaked out that on Bonner's orders the allegations were being probed by RCMP Inspector, W.J. Butler." But, even though Inspector Butler's report stated that there appeared to be evidence of wrongdoing, the Attorney-General didn't act on Butler's recommendations or make the report public.

The Social Credit government stood fast throughout the boisterous controversy, but on February 27, 1956, the storm abated briefly when Sommers stood in the House and gave a speech, later called a diatribe by some, that "wielded a whitewash brush" on himself and a "tar brush" on his accusers, according to Brooks.

The speech only added fuel to the fire and the arguments raged on. Sommers continued to maintain that the allegations against him were "part of a campaign of destruction backed by the cut-and-run logging interests," and further, were backed by the "Liberals and certain newspapers that had been presenting the most dirty and slanted news coverage in the history of B.C." He alleged that Eversfield "had stolen documents, tried to shake down his employer, then fled to California."

Sommers still denied any charges of bribery, saying "I have never used my office for personal gain, directly or indirectly, morally or technically," and "The charge is as phoney as the man who made it."

But things had now gone too far. The province was aroused.

On February 27, 1956, the premier called Sommers into his office and asked for his resignation. But the political storm was far from over.

During a "riotous all-night sitting three days later, Opposition members demanded a judicial inquiry and the resignation of both Sommers and Bonner as MLAs. Social Credit still sat tight, and the session ended in a stalemate."

The wily Premier called a snap election that summer of 1956. Sommers had managed to stall Sturdy's case in the courts so the public wouldn't hear the facts. The Rossland-Trail Social Credit Association was unanimous in Sommers nomination; in fact his nominator called him "a small school teacher who has emerged to prominence . . . a first class asset to the province." Voters in his riding dubbed him "Honest Bob," and "hoisted him up on their shoulders, cheering and singing, 'For He's A Jolly Good Fellow'."

Incredibly, Sommers was re-elected, as was the Social Credit government. But the campaign was not without its moments. Premier Bennett was hearing some dirty words like "smear, propaganda, dirty politics," in his own invulnerable Okanagan Valley riding of Kelowna. Bonner was heckled in Ocean Falls, but kept his silence.

Some comic relief occurred in North Vancouver, where Social Credit's nominee Newton Steacy was "tub-thumping about being proud of our record as a party that doesn't allow anything dishonest." And his running mate, Mel Bryan, who a year later was to cross the floor of the House when he changed his mind on the Sommers case, was crying: "If there had been any evidence, it could have been put before a magistrate months ago. Liberals Gregory and Sturdy are derelict in their duty as members of the bar, or guilty of scandalous rumour-mongering."

Because the press kept taking shots at him, Sommers was becoming worried that the opposition would start using heavier ammunition. A letter from his lawyer went out to the opposition MLAs threatening action for contempt of court if they commented on the case while he was suing Sturdy for slander. Tory leader Deane Finlayson and the press chose to ignore the threat. Sommers' lawyer attempted to have those who publicly discussed the case charged with contempt, but Mr. Justice J.O. Wilson "came down heavily on the side of free speech and a free press," noting that by becoming a public and political figure, Sommers "had offered himself to the electorate well knowing that his past would have to be probed . . . It ill-becomes him to complain of a set of charges already known to the public . . . "

Bonner continued to maintain his silence. As Attorney-General, he refused to publish RCMP Inspector Butler's report, in spite of continuous media pressure to release it to the public.

Meanwhile, the case simmered on for yet another year, and in the Legislature a weakened Opposition demanded the Butler report, Bonner's resignation, and a judicial inquiry. They got nowhere, and neither did Sturdy, whose requests for permission to see certain bank accounts to support his accusations were denied.

The end came, finally, after 22 months when the Supreme Court of Canada ordered Sommers to "put up or shut up." He countered by claiming he was too sick to continue. He brought a doctor's certification of his illness, but it was thrown out of court as "worthless evidence," and he was "ordered to appear for a medical examination." But Sommers disappeared, and the case was dismissed.

Sturdy had won by default and now the files in the case could be made public.

Meanwhile, Bonner went to Europe on a "trade mission." In his absence, the files in the case were made public for the first time. Premier Bennett needed Bonner's advice on stonewalling to help him weather the on-and-off storms of controversy. Messages streamed back and forth across the Atlantic. Bonner told reporters, "there would not be a judicial inquiry, nor would the Butler report be released." Then he seemed to change his mind after talking to Premier Bennett and his acting Forests Minister. He told reporters: "An inquiry is not ruled out."

Finally, on November 1, 1957, "a haggard, grey-faced Premier acted," wrote Brooks. Bennett announced that a commissioner,

"Honest Bob" Sommers accompanied by the R.C.M.P.

B.C. PROVINCIAL ARCHIVES

Chief Justice Gordon Sloan, would be appointed to "probe the Sommers allegations." He stressed that the "probe was on the recommendation of Bonner."

Sommers, hiding out somewhere in the U.S., was busy making a tape recording for a broadcast, in which for the first time he mentioned "loans," not bribes. He told the public that he had "sufficient evidence to back his story," and would "genuinely welcome criminal prosecution." But he was still "hiding out" on November 12, 1957, the first sitting day of the Sloan probe.

The commission adjourned after only half an hour on the very day that Sommers sneaked into town through back streets and attempted to hide in the safety of his home. The next day he invited the reporters in. But, except to speak of his illness, he didn't have much new to tell.

Eight days later, the RCMP arrested Sommers at the breakfast table in his own house. They had also arrested C.D. Schultz and H.W. Gray in Vancouver the same day, and the Toronto police were looking for John Gray, Wick's brother, another accused member of the alleged conspiracy. The police claimed they were acting on the direct orders of Attorney-General Bonner, the highest law enforcement officer in the land, and the one-time friend and colleague of three of the men. The charges were conspiracy and bribery.

These arrests came 707 days after Eversfield and Sturdy had made their initial accusations. The preliminary hearing was set for February 12, 1958, and many hidden facts and evidence would be made public.

Bonner was losing his popularity among his Social Credit supporters. A political revolt seemed to be brewing. It became open revolt in January. Mel Bryan, who had defended Sommers in North Vancouver in 1956, now demanded Bonner's resignation. But, of course, Bonner didn't resign. Instead, Bryan crossed the floor of the House, a dramatic act that had a serious effect on Premier Bennett.

Still the tide of support ran against Bonner. Finally, in March, the Opposition moved for a vote of non-confidence against him, and three Socred MLAs left the floor of the House so they wouldn't have to vote on the motion.

During the debate, Premier Bennett tried to defend his actions, saying that he had been acting on the advice of "some senior civil servants."

But now, Bennett said the government was anxious to clear up the whole bribery mess, and when the civil case was dismissed, he decided to act to ensure that justice prevailed. So the arrests were made. The court would decide. The storm centre shifted from Victoria and moved into the Vancouver law courts, amid great press speculation and public discussion.

One of the most contentious issues was of the stalling tactics of Premier W.A.C. Bennett and Attorney-General Robert Bonner. But after the Butler Report was made public, many people said it "proved that the Bennett government should not have delayed for nearly two years before laying charges against Sommers."

One of the key sections of the RCMP report concludes:

> Having spent a considerable number of hours questioning Eversfield (the original source of the information that eventually led to Sommers' conviction), and checking his story against the documents, [Inspector Butler] feels that there is definite indication of wrong-doing on the part of Pacific Coast Services Ltd., R.E. Sommers, C.D. Schultz, and B.C. Forests Products Ltd., but as to how far this can be proved remains for further investigation.
>
> In order to obtain a correct picture, what is really required is a complete audit of books and bank accounts of Pacific Coast Services Ltd., Evergreen Lumber Sales Ltd., and an examination of the bank accounts of H.W. Gray, R.E. Sommers, J.H. Gray, C.D. Schultz and B.C. Forest Products Ltd.

It was public pressure and the press that had finally forced Bennett and Bonner to take action. Sturdy declared that Attorney-General Bonner should have done in 1955 what he did in 1957.

However, even though the trial had begun, the quest for justice was tedious. There was the alleged three-way split of bribe money between Pacific Coast Services Ltd., C.D. Schultz and his company, and Sommers. Eversfield had presented one document showing Sommers had received $17,610. To come in the future was $11,350 as Sommers' share of $45,000 paid to C.D. Schultz' company by the Tahsis Company; $20,000 as his share of $80,000 to be paid by B.C. Forest Products Ltd."

Judge J.O. Wilson commented on the alleged financial transactions in this case as "curious," "unusual," and "devious;" adding there was a 'rather conspicuous lack of use of cheques" in deals involving some of the defendants.

Then there was Sommers' story about one of his "loans." The court heard the incredible story that he had gone into his bank to inquire about the "loan" in question, only to hear the bank manager ask, "What loan?" Apparently, it had been paid some months earlier, but the bank manager couldn't say by whom.

During the trial, rumours and accusations were continuous. The mere fact that Sommers, who was continually broke, was represented by the late Angelo Branca, Q.C., one of Vancouver's most expensive criminal lawyers, was enough to keep a cloud of suspicion over the whole affair. It was never disclosed who had paid Branca's fees.

The Sommers' trial was a tangled skein of evidence. Including six adjournments, court records showed that 14 court reporters had taken down and transcribed more than 1,000,000 words of testimony. Ten of Vancouver's highest paid lawyers and Crown Prosecutor Vic Dwyer and his assistants had examined and argued over more than 1,000 documents. The jury, nine men and three women, after listening to evidence for 79 days, deliberated for 50 hours. But when it was all over there remained a puzzle which was never fully put together and one which will never be assembled now to give the full picture.

Indeed, in an unusual pronouncement, Mr. Justice Wilson reportedly said the jury had done such a tremendous job in the complex trial that he was going to recommend to the Attorney-General's Department that they be given a substantial grant, even if it took special legislation. He said no matter what they got, it could never repay them for what they had gone through. The jury payment of $6 a day was almost "disgracefully inadequate." It was so small that it could mean bankruptcy for a person with a small business or working for wages who was called on to judge a lengthy case. He was sure that if they were ever called for jury duty again and didn't want to serve, the presiding judge would probably excuse them if they told him they had been on the Sommers trial panel.

The jury was presented with so many incredulous and conflicting pieces of information, it was a wonder they came up with any verdicts at all, but they did.

The verdicts were finally presented almost a year later, in November, 1958. The jury had deliberated for more than 50 hours, disagreeing on some of the charges against each of the defendants. In addition, five of the charges against Sommers for allegedly receiving some of the "loans" were withdrawn at the direction of the judge.

The jury found Sommers guilty on five counts of receiving bribes from Wick Gray in a conspiracy to collect and split bribes from firms willing to pay for Forest Management Licences while Sommers was in office. There was disagreement by the jury on a further two counts.

Gray was convicted on eight out of 10 original counts of conspiracy and giving bribes to Sommers. Again, there were two "disagreement verdicts" in Gray's case. In addition, both Gray and Sommers were convicted of a "general conspiracy to give and receive bribes."

Of Gray's two companies, Pacific Coast Services was convicted on eight counts of conspiracy and fined a total of $15,250, and Evergreen Lumber Sales was convicted on two counts and fined $4,000. There were additional disagreement verdicts in their case, as well.

Charles D. Schultz, Bob Schultz' brother, was found not guilty on four counts, and the jury disagreed on a further five counts. The same non-verdict results were found in the case of his company, C.D. Schultz & Co. Ltd.

B.C. Forest Products Ltd. was pronounced not guilty on five counts, with a disagreement verdict on one count.

John M. Gray, a director of one of his brother's companies, was found not guilty on two counts, with disagreement verdicts on a further two counts.

Before passing sentence on former Forests Minister Robert E. Sommers and his partner in crime, H. Wilson Gray, Mr. Justice J.O. Wilson read a prepared statement to them and the court. The most significant comment reads:

> I do not enjoy hitting men when they are down as both of you men are, but this is an exceptional case and requires comment. The jury...not I, has found you both scoundrels. The evidence on which that finding must be based reveals that both of you have befouled the political and moral atmosphere of this province for a period of many years, resorting to every sort and shape of device to conceal your iniquities.
>
> The harm you, Sommers, have done to our traditional respect for government will, I hope, be slight, because, thank God, the sort of behaviour of which you have been convicted is not just exceptional but unique in our political history."

Sommers received a sentence of one year's imprisonment on each of five counts, to be served consecutively for a total of five years.

Wilson Gray received the same five-year jail term for his offences, as the additional three counts he was convicted of were served concurrently with the other sentences imposed.

Socred Irvine Corbett, MLA for Yale, and one of the backbenchers who broke with the government over Attorney-General Robert Bonner's handling of the case, posted $24,000 bail bond for Sommers. This released him from Oakalla prison pending appeal. But Sommers was unsuccessful in his appeal.

After serving two years and four months "Honest Bob" was released from Gordon Head Penitentiary. Behind bars, he had become an accomplished piano tuner. In fact he tuned a baby grand piano at my home in the Cinnabar Valley, just south of Nanaimo, shortly after he started his new business. Now 80 years old, he lives in Errington, a small semi-rural community west of

Parksville on Vancouver Island. His business, Sommers Piano & Organ Sales Ltd. in Parksville, has been taken over by his son.

Everyone was exhausted, and emotionally and financially drained by the time the Sommers case was finished.

Alfred Bull, Q.C. said his client, C.D.Schultz, was a "ruined man" because of allegations against him and his company. Bull described his client as a "Vancouver-born son of a late County Court judge, educated in private and public schools, a UBC graduate, army veteran and successful businessman." He related that Schultz' company had grossed more that $2 million in a seven-year period "...including $386,000 in fees received in 1957, a year during which there was a freeze on the issuance of Forest Management Licences." Bull added that Schultz and his companies had received practically nothing since the indictment, saying that the business had melted from a personnel of more than 100 down to three.

Things didn't turn out as badly for Robert Bonner. After 16 years as Attorney-General, he resigned and in 1968 became Senior Vice-President of Adminstration for MacMillan Bloedel, the province's immense forest giant. Four years later he was appointed President and Chief Executive Officer, a position he held for one year. In April 1973, Bonner was named Chairman, and one year later he confirmed his resignation from that corporation. Then, just days after the Socreds defeated the NDP on December 22, 1975, Bonner was given the job of Chairman and Chief Executive Officer of B.C. Hydro by former premier W.A.C. Bennett's son Bill Bennett, the new Premier of British Columbia.

Schultz and Sommers weren't the only ones who had a bad time because of this case. Judge Wilson reported he'd had his life threatened the day before the verdicts were read. He said the caller, "speaking in a cultured voice," warned that the attempt on his life would be made in his Kerrisdale home in Vancouver. Earlier in the trial, he said he'd received poison-pen letters.

Even though the judge immediately made provision for the "disagreement verdicts" to come to retrial, the Attorney-General's office did not proceed. Why? To this day, over 19 original charges in this case have never been resolved. They remain hanging like a spectre over both government and industry. Perhaps some day the truth will surface. But so far, the Sommers' case remains B.C.'s Watergate.

The entire sorry, devious and stone-walling episode brought great dishonour to B.C.'s government and seriously damaged the reputation of our Forest Ministry, causing longstanding distrust in their method of granting Tree Farm Licences. Justice was seen to be done, but was all justice done?

CHAPTER THREE

Honesty Counts

Although I never knew Sommers very well, I was much better acquainted with Ray Williston. And, in my opinion, Sommers was a cull who had to be removed while Williston was a healthy young specimen who contributed much to forestry in British Columbia.

I first met Ray Williston in the summer of 1949 on a flooded street in Prince George in north-central B.C., a growing logging and industrial city. There had been a horrific rainstorm. The southeast area of Prince George along the swollen Fraser River was under several feet of muddy water.

On our Cessna 195 radio, Brother Tom and I heard a radio news announcer report that the only bridge over the Fraser was unsafe and closed to all traffic. The two main foundations supporting the bridge were being undermined by the flood waters and the structure was in danger of collapse.

"Maybe we should drop in there and see if they need help," Tom said, as we flew toward Vancouver after visiting friends at Vanderhoof. We circled low over the south end of the town and landed on the river, then taxied our float plane up one of the flooded streets. It must have been an extraordinary sight, as I think of it now: two men wading out into the muddy flood water, which was about six inches above their knees.

Ray introduced himself with a big grin and a handshake, saying, "I'm a school teacher here. I've just sent my students to higher ground."

"Is there anyone in trouble?" Tom asked.

"Not right now, thank you," Ray answered. "But when you get to Quesnel, please ask the Highways department to send up some power boats so we can get people and supplies across this flooding river."

The phone lines in Prince George were either down in the river, or otherwise out of order. Delivering that message was our good deed for the day.

In August, 1989, Ray and I met again at the Sechelt Festival of the Written Arts, where Mrs. Williston is one of its organizers. It was then that Ray Williston, now retired, agreed to come to Nanaimo where I live and do a taped interview.

When I asked Ray how he became involved with forestry, he told me people usually don't believe his explanation. He had been Minister of Education for almost three years when Robert Sommers, the Minister of Lands and Forests, got himself into trouble. When Sommers continued to refuse to answer questions in the House, Premier W.A.C. Bennett lost his cool and jumped to his feet at 4:30 in the afternoon of February 27, 1956. He called for an evening sitting, then adjourned the House. He immediately ordered Bob Sommers to his office and demanded his resignation. The letter was typed and lying on the Premier's desk. All Sommers had to do was sign his name. This he did without a word, then turned and walked out.

W.A.C. then contacted Ray Williston and Ken Kiernan. They were to be in his office in 10 minutes.

Ray well remembers the phone call: "W.A.C. sounded grumpy. I wondered what was on his mind. Arriving at his office, we learned that he had already phoned Government House to make the necessary arrangements with the Lieutenant-Governor. His car and chauffeur were standing by. Shortly after five that same afternoon, I was sworn in as the new Minister of Lands and Forests, and Ken Kiernan became the Minister of Mines."

At that evening's sitting of the House, Premier Bennett announced the appointment of his two new Cabinet ministers and assured the MLAs there would be some answers for the Forests estimates debate the following day. Sommers hadn't been giving the House satisfactory responses to the Opposition's questions, and the press was in full cry.

Working all night, a good many problems had to be reviewed. Ray was able to have Sommers' secretary and her assistant work along with him until 6 a.m. They explained the proposed Lands and Forests budget to him, and filled him in on the circumstances surrounding some of the allegations of bribery of which Sommers was suspected.

This was the first time the British Columbia government ever sat through an all night session, and Ray had had little or no sleep during his first 48 hours as Forests Minister. That was the auspicious and grinding start to his 16 years of guiding the B.C. Forest Service through some major changes. And it was a fast start in more ways than one. Chief Justice Gordon Sloan had just handed down his recommendations of the second Royal Commission on Forestry. Implementing those recommendations was the immediate responsibility of the new Minister.

I asked Ray if that was the start of Forest Management Licences. He replied, "No, Forest Management Licences came about as a result of the first Sloan Commission Report in 1945. Licence #1 was issued by E.T. Kenney in May 1948. That was during the Liberal and Conservative coalition government when Kenney was Minister of Forests and MLA for Prince Rupert. That Forest Management Licence was a huge area of virgin timber that included the drainage systems of both the Skeena and Nass rivers. The licence was issued to Columbia Cellulose for their proposed pulp mill at Port Edward, a few miles south of Prince Rupert. That same government issued another nine management licences before the Social Credit government was elected in 1952.

"For some reason, all the Forest Management Licences were renamed as Tree Farm Licences at a later date, and remain so to this day. Even back then, there were great concerns about the system. Every lumber and pulp mill in the province was lobbying to get one."

That was true. At the time of Williston's appointment, the Sommers bribery case was revolving around the granting of one

46

management licence in particular, FML #22 to B.C. Forest Products on May 18, 1955. Fraud was suspected and eventually proven, although B.C. Forest Products was never found guilty. The disagreement verdict delivered by the jury has, to this day, never been resolved one way or another.

When Williston went through Sommers' records, which he did in great detail, he told me Sommers had "shuffled the deck," then considered some applications and wouldn't consider others. He said he couldn't see any apparent reason why Sommers should have acted in that way.

One of Sloan's main recommendations to Williston was that he should deal with the Forest Management Licences that were already in the process of being awarded, both at the Coast and in the Interior. Williston went on to issue several fairly large licences that had been recommended for the Interior. When those were dealt with, he temporarily closed off the awarding of Forest Management Licences. Williston had followed Sloan's recommendations to the letter.

There was one shattering experience for the new Forests Minister concerning the Powell River Company. Blondie Swanson in Squamish was president of what was then known as the Western Forest Management Association, composed of independent smaller loggers. Swanson and his association felt they were being cut off from timber—their livelihood—with many jobs at stake. He and his lawyer, Ron Howard, manoeuvered the Powell River application into the courts and managed to have the proceedings tied up for over a year.

After the courts ruled in favour of the Powell River Company, Williston admitted he had learned a great deal about people and Forest Management Licences. Shortly after Powell River received the licence, rumours started to the effect that the Western Forest Management Association and Blondie Swanson had been partly financed by MacMillan Bloedel to try to prevent or stall the application in order to frustrate and cut down Powell River's expansion plans.

47

"H.R. MacMillan came over to see me the following week." Ray explained. "He was a member of the Board of Directors and also Chairman of the Finance Committee of M&B. He'd come over quite often and, at times, would try to educate me about good forestry practices and other matters. This day, after a handshake, he said: 'Mr. Minister, there is a horrible rumour going around that MacMillan financed Western Forest Management to hold up the awarding of a forest management licence to Powell River. I want to tell you that is an outright lie.'"

"I told him that I'd also heard this and he shouldn't worry," Ray said.

Next day at MacMillan's finance meeting in Vancouver, when he informed the board members that he'd been over to see the Minister of Forests and denied this rumour, silence fell over the room. It was then he learned his company had indeed issued a cheque to Blondie Swanson. MacMillan was mortified. He was a man of firm convictions and what he told his Board we may never know; we can only imagine.

"That was the last time H.R. ever visited me in my office. He must have been ashamed because it appeared that he didn't know what was going on in his own department. He had told me something he thought to be true, then found out it wasn't. The old man had great integrity and he insisted that Ernie Shorter, an executive vice-president, come over and straighten things out."

Apart from the crooked goings on in Victoria, Williston was starting to straighten out northern B.C. logging. From 1953 to 1965, Garner Bros. Cariboo Ltd. was logging on Western Plywood's long-term timber sale south of Quesnel. During this 15-year sale, scaling and stumpage were calculated on the old "board measure" basis. Log tops were cut off at eight inches in diameter, leaving a considerable amount of wasted wood. This might have been good for plywood manufacturing, but it certainly wasn't good utilization.

When the timber sale was re-issued, top sizes went down to four inches and stump diameters were lowered accordingly. From that time on everything was measured by the new cubic scale. This was the start of the Pulp Harvest Area system.

So we became involved with Williston's plans for future pulp mills, the new Chip-n-Saw sawmill systems and all the other changes that were going on in the Interior timber business. We just happened to be there and were caught up at the very beginning, and right on through until four of the northern pulp mills had been built and were operating. Most of this new system of better utilization can pretty well be attributed to the foresight and determination of Ray Williston, the school teacher who learned forestry the hard way.

I asked Ray what got him started on the pulp mill program and the complete utilization of the poorer northern forests, a program which had vast economic benefits for the province.

"It all started in my office in Victoria when Tom Wright walked in. Tom was teaching forestry at the University of British Columbia and my mother had a boarding house out in Point Grey. He was one of her boarders, and that was when we became friends. My door was always open to Tom.

"Also when he visited me he had been Dean of Forestry at U.B.C. Anyway, he walked into my office this day and stunned me with one simple question: 'Mr. Minister, in your Prince George Forest District, what percentage of the wood do you think gets into the boxcars for shipment?'"

"My calculated guess is between 50 and 60 percent."

"'Would you believe 25 percent? You're trying to run an industry on 25 percent of the available fibre, while wasting 75 percent. That's what you're doing, and it won't work.'"

Williston thought Tom Wright must be completely wrong. Such waste was incredible. He went up to Prince George to see for himself. He got in touch with Harold Moffatt, who was then head of the economic development group for the Prince George region. Harold had also been Ray's campaign manager when he was first elected for the Social Credit Party in August 1952, when the party stunned B.C. and Canada by coming to power, against all odds as a 'nothing' group.

Williston and Moffatt decided they had better see what Larry deGrace, a consulting forester in the Prince George area, thought about the idea of a pulp mill at Prince George. "Tom Wright tells me that we're wasting about 75 percent of the usable wood fibre around here," Williston challenged Larry when they met.

"Yes, I'd say that's about right," Larry admitted.

The incredible was true.

"That wasted material could run a sizable pulp mill right here in Prince George," Moffatt suggested.

"Well, about the only thing this wasted wood can be used for is pulp chips," deGrace agreed.

"Could you do an engineering study and give me a report?" Williston asked. It was a good request, as deGrace had his own consulting business and was already advising most of the larger sawmills in the area.

"Who is going to pay for it?" deGrace asked.

Moffatt volunteered to raise the money, but after scrounging around some of the local mill owners for the rest of the afternoon all he came up with was a meager $200. They came back to see Larry and asked, "Would you prepare us a consultant's report on the utilization of waste, including a pulp mill and its effects on this district for $200?"

In retrospect, that $200 offer was almost an insult.

When Larry said 'yes', that had to be the best $200 ever spent in British Columbia. This report was taken to Victoria and read by Williston when he made his opening speech for his next Forestry estimates. It explained in detail how all that waste could be converted into chips and used for pulp, creating hundreds of new jobs. The outcome was an immediate start on some sample chip production from independent sawmills over a wide area of northern B.C.

These sample chips were shipped by boxcar to pulp mills at the Coast and other areas to determine if they were of good quality. The answer was a definite 'yes'. Yet some of the larger lumber mills said that it wasn't possible to run a pulp industry on waste.

A forestry magazine ran an editorial about Williston saying, "This guy Williston must be out of his cotton-picking mind."

The lumber producers around Prince George were wary, and organized the area so that the big pulp mills couldn't go in and compete for their timber supply. However, all the mills agreed they would sell their chips to the pulp mills at fair market prices. Part of Williston's plan was to make enough low-grade timber available to the pulp mills without taking the better quality trees away from the lumber mills. That wasn't easy.

At the time when Williston was considering giving out incentives to the lumber mills and doing his best to figure out a scheme to utilize all that unmarketable timber, along came Ian Mahood. He had just resigned as one of MacMillan Bloedel's chief foresters and started his own consulting business. The Brynlesens had recently sold their mining interests north of Prince George and bought up several sawmills east of town. They had worked with Noranda Mines and were now showing interest in starting up their own pulp mill. Mahood had been hired to do a feasibility study for them.

Williston's ministry and Mahood, with the help of Larry de-Grace, outlined on maps the areas that, because they contained the poorer quality trees, were to become pulp harvesting areas. They rearranged the Public Working Circles in the better timber stands and the poorer timber was set aside for the pulp mills. This would guarantee that the pulp mills had sufficient material for chips, in case there wasn't enough coming in from the lumber mills. Working as a team, government and free enterprise were able to put together a plan to satisfy just about everyone.

When Williston heard the Bentleys of Canadian Forest Products were considering the possibility of building a pulp mill in northern Alberta, he immediately went to see them. Poldi Bentley consulted his chief forester, Tom Wright, who told him his firm had already made a study and there was plenty of good material for a sizable pulp mill around Prince George. Ian Mahood explained how the pulp harvest areas would satisfy the financiers' demand for an assured wood supply, so loans could be made.

Williston then called together the doubtful, ruggedly independent private sawmill operators and explained what the Forest Service was prepared to do.

"If you fellows can upgrade your mills to process all these smaller trees, you will only be charged the same stumpage as the pulp mills," a deal so good it would be hard to reject.

Though this was not made law, Williston gave his word and the mill operators accepted it.

"You will have to bark all of these smaller logs, just as a pulp mill does. You can take the lumber out, but the chips must be sold for pulp to a local pulp mill. Remember that small wood will only cost you 55 cents per 100 cubic feet and the B.C. Forest Service guarantees you will have sufficient timber on these terms for a minimum of 10 years from the time we start. This should take care of the borrowing power you might need from the bank for new equipment and give you plenty of time to pay it off." Williston was working well with both the big and small operators.

Out of the blue, a young electrical engineer, Ernie Runnion, showed up from Shelton, Washington where he had been working in a small sawmill. He showed Williston a rough plan of what he called a "chip-n-saw."

"You just bark the logs and send them through the chipper and gang saws. The chips come out one chute and the lumber out of another," this young American explained. This idea had enormous possibilities for cutting small logs into either lumber or chips—a dream machine. With Williston's blessing and encouragement, this inventor went to a firm in Vancouver, then known as Canadian Car Pacific Ltd., and they helped plan and put together a completely new type of mill for cutting and utilizing all the small Interior trees. The old ways were gone forever.

At Quesnel, John Ernst, an old sawmill man, had acquired sufficient courage and cash to try out this new mill arrangement in the 1950s. His was the first chip-n-saw to be used in the Pacific Northwest. It didn't take him long to realize that the logs, when barked, had to be sorted to size. He could then run a good number of the same sized logs at any one time. This way he didn't have to waste time continually adjusting the saws and chipper. Even a one-inch difference in log size didn't slow production. The revolution had arrived!

By this time, the foundations had already been laid for the first pulp mill in Prince George. By the mid '60s, there were dozens of chip-n-saw mills operating in the northern Interior, giving the pulp mills sufficient chips for their total requirements. These new chip-n-saw mills became real money-makers for everyone who used them. The pioneer, John Ernst, made himself more than a million dollars in just a few years. Lumbermen and businessmen were arriving from all over North America to watch these little mills perform. Most of them were amazed to see the high quality of chips and lumber produced from all this haywire timber.

Although MacMillan's executives had originally lobbied against pulp mills in the north country, it wasn't long before some of their foresters came to see what was going on. Larry Harris and John Hemmingsen were investigating the possibility of getting similar mills going in their operations in the southern U.S. pine forests.

"I never did get much cooperation from coastal logging operations in the processing of the smaller timber, with the exception of Herb Doman of Duncan on Vancouver Island," Ray recalled. "Herb started out as a trucker and hauled lumber from the Interior to the coast. He used to marvel at the quality and quantity of lumber and chips that were produced from all these small junky trees. By following the example set in the Interior, Herb Doman eventually made enough money to buy his own pulp mills."

Using this small timber made it absolutely necessary to change scaling procedures from the old B.C. board-foot measure system to the cubic scale. Everyone got a truer measurement by doing this. That change came in the late '50s and early '60s, but it wasn't until 1966 that scaling by weight was recognized and accepted. To control the truck weights, the government put in weigh scales, and it became law that all logging trucks using public highways must be weighed. About every tenth load was check-scaled in the mill yards to get a weight conversion average from the different areas. Two scalers did this, one paid by the mill, the other by the B.C. Forest Service. Those scalers, measuring quantity, had to be government-licenced. This made scaling less dangerous, more accurate and much less expensive than scaling in the woods where the logging and loading took place.

The mills sold their lumber on a board-foot basis. So McMillan Contracting Ltd. near Lone Butte to the southeast of 100 Mile House, decided to install narrower-gauge saws, and they actually increased their conversion factor of 5.5 to 7.5 board-feet per cubic foot of scaled logs. This put about 20 percent more money in their pockets. The wide-gauge saws wasted 3/8 of an inch of good wood every time a board was cut.

The up-and-down industry was flourishing; everyone was happy.

The McMillans told Williston they were sometimes getting a conversion factor as high as eight board feet out of every cubic foot of log scale. This gave them 45 percent more profit on their logs. When Williston told other mill operators about this they didn't believe him. To prove his point, two government scalers were sent to the McMillan mill. They measured every log going into the mill and every board-foot of lumber coming out. They randomly picked the logs. During the ten-day trial period, the conversion averaged 7.96 board-feet per cubic foot of logs. When this lumber went through the planer to improve its marketability, it just had to be brushed to smooth out the edges. The McMillan brothers were the happiest operators in the province!

During the years Williston was Minister of Lands and Forests, there had been many arguments. Dr. Peter Pearse, a University of B.C. professor, was "gung ho" to have more tree farm licences regardless of the poor showing they had made in creating a sustained yield forest complex in the province. During the 30 or more years they had been in operation, the standing timber stocks of B.C. were being depleted at an alarming rate. It looked like in about another 30 to 40 years the most we could expect to leave our children would be second-growth timber. Something was very wrong. Royal Commissioner Sloan's plan for sustained yield was not working. In some areas, the big manufacturing outfits were raping the forests at about twice the rate that they were planting seedlings for reforestation.

Williston summed it up. "Peter Pearse had always been strong on Tree Farm Licences. He actually talked himself into becoming a one-man Royal Commissioner for the NDP government." Williston had little use for his political opposition.

In 1972, the Social Credit government was defeated by the NDP. Bob Williams was appointed Minister of Lands and Forests. He was a clever, sharp-tongued, no-nonsense socialist from a Vancouver riding. Without delay, he did away with the 55-cent stumpage for pulp salvage wood. He also raised the minimum stumpage rate on saw logs. Consequently, when the lumber and pulp market went into a slump, there was little revenue being collected for the government from the forest resource. Most of the smaller operators had to either shut down or go broke. These two changes took away the stumpage cushion available when the market and prices were bad.

"It's a good thing that type of government thinking only went on for a few years," Ray suggested.

Even today, Williston thinks about forestry improvement. When I talked to him in 1990, he was consulting for Kootenay Forest Products, investigating the Ponderosa pine in the West Kootenays. Their mills were cutting cants—partially milled logs in a rough squared condition to be finished into lumber later or to be sold and shipped to the eastern United States for slicing. The value of these cants, when sliced, was 10 times greater than when cut into dimension lumber at the mill site.

"I got some samples of this pine wood," Ray recalled, "packed it in a suitcase, and took off for General Woods & Veneers in the eastern United States. There, these pine cants were being sliced in the largest slicer on the North American continent. This is a company owned by a man named Marcel Oliphant, who lives in Montreal but has many of his plants in the United States. He's one hard-nosed businessman, if ever there was one, but he really knows the lumber industry."

Williston tried to talk him into building a slicing plant in British Columbia, where most of the good pine grows. The benefits to the B.C. forest industry would be great. But Marcel couldn't get the necessary commitment from the B.C. government, so B.C. doesn't have a slicing plant yet.

Both men agreed that with some reasonable commitment for pine logs from the Forests Ministry, the people of B.C. could well triple their stumpage income from Ponderosa pine.

"He hasn't come out here yet, but he still keeps in touch with me," Ray said. "He's put plants in China and other countries, but he can't get the needed cooperation here. It's hard to believe the dollar value he gets out of one good pine log. It's thousands of dollars compared to a few hundred if it's cut into dimension lumber. The slices are mostly used in the manufacture of high grade furniture. He's developed a market for our pine and red cedar to where it's a major part of his business. He found that the tropical hardwoods, which have to be shipped in from long distances, were not selling as well as the pine and cedar. Consequently, his warehouses were jammed with sliced mahogany."

When the palatial Pan-Pacific Hotel in Vancouver was being built, Marcel Oliphant came out from Montreal to bid on all the wood-finishing and landed the contract. His was the lowest bid because enough of the specified mahogany was already sliced and stacked in his warehouses.

"We have never really taken top value out of our wood here in British Columbia," the former Forests Minister explained. "But we should start, and the sooner the better. Herb Doman is getting into it at his new Duke Point mill in Nanaimo. They are sorting out every bit of clear lumber and making it into high-priced finishing material. Some of this clear finishing material sells for up to 10 times the dollar value of 2x4s and other such dimension lumber.

"Getting back to our forests: there are certain areas that can best be clearcut and certain areas that should be selectively logged. There are thousands of acres in the northern part of our province where the jackpine grows only to about six inches in diameter at ground level, and not more than 90 feet tall in 100 years or more. It's the slow growth that makes the best lumber and pulp in the world. I believe this should be clearcut and immediately replanted. I feel quite sure these forests, if properly cared for, will give a better yield than the first crop, and in a much shorter time period. On the mainland coast from near Ocean Falls on up to Kitimat, there is less logging going on now than there has been at any time during the last 50 years," he explained. "The trees there are deteriorating and most of that old dead-top timber should be harvested. A good percentage may have to be logged by helicopter, but it certainly should not be left to just rot or become a fire hazard.

"Now, with self-loading, self-dumping log barges, it solves some of the problems of moving logs from the west coast of Vancouver Island, the Queen Charlottes, and the exposed mainland coast. Along the west coast, you're bucking huge open-ocean swells, so towing logs in flat booms is out of the question. If you're a gyppo north of Vancouver Island, you have to accumulate enough logs in one place to bring in and load one of the huge log barges. This eliminates most of the smaller gyppos, even though there is a lot of good timber in the area that should be harvested.

"That's why I fought so hard to keep Ocean Falls in production," Williston said. "It was the only pulp mill in that area the loggers could sell to. In that up-coast area, a good percentage of the logs are only fit for pulp. There are going to have to be centres like Ocean Falls where the pulp logs can be sorted out and converted into chips, then barged to the southern pulp and paper mills. When people say we're running out of timber, they really don't understand what is available using helicopters or long skylines."

"Were you involved in the proposed development at Stewart near the head of Portland Canal and north of Prince Rupert?" I asked Ray. "It was on the way to becoming one of the finest pulp mills and sea ports on the west coast of North America."

"Yes, I was, Joe," Ray replied. "Stewart was and still is an ideal place for a good pulp mill. The decadence of that rain forest behind Stewart is a disgrace to our province. Fifty percent of it is over-mature and rotting. It is absolutely necessary to have a pulp mill to utilize that sort of timber. The timber supply there was already allotted by 1970, and would have made a mill both practical and profitable.

"Cyril Dawkin of Nanaimo had everything surveyed. The townsite, power plant and shipping docks were all ready to go. When the NDP government took over in 1972, they cut the timber tenure to one year and nobody would touch the financing with a 10-foot pole. The entire project just fell apart.

"As Minister of Lands and Forests, one of the last things I did in preparation for the pulp mill at Stewart was to get the bridge built over the Nass River near Meziadin Lake. That bridge effectively opened up the road between Hazelton, Kitwanga and Stewart. It was part of the overall plan for a deep-sea harbour and the development of Stewart as a manufacturing town."

In August 1972, Williston cut the ribbon that opened the bridge over the Meziadin River. That same year, his government was defeated in a September election. Ray must be credited with spearheading some of the most innovative schemes our timber industry has ever known.

To show further evidence of Williston's long-range planning, in the early 1960s he set aside an endowment area of some 2,100 acres of unsurveyed Crown land on Cranbrook Hill southwest of Prince George, to be reserved for a university some time in the future.

The Social Credit government recently added another 500 acres of Crown property to the northeast portion of the endowment area to allow for a better view, better drainage and easier access for roads and services. The new University of Northern British Columbia (UNBC) will occupy a portion of this site where there will be sufficient forested land to teach intensive forestry in all its different phases.

When I was in Prince George in late June 1991, I visited their temporary offices downtown. The new university's first president, Professor Geoffrey Weller, had already been appointed. The main campus should be ready for occupancy in the fall of 1993. However, they hope to start some programs at both the undergraduate and graduate level in the fall of 1992 in temporary facilities. This new centre of learning is due in part to the far-sightedness of Ray Williston.

In spite of the bad feelings left by the Sommers case, Ray Williston was able to re-establish a sense of trust during his 16 years in office. Ironically, this highly intelligent man will probably be remembered as the namesake of Williston Lake behind the massive Peace River dam and hydro plant rather than for his dedication to bettering the lives of British Columbians through his no-nonsense approach to the logging, lumbering and pulp industries.

CHAPTER FOUR

One Man's Protest

Government policy always has repercussions on the common man. And when government favours the big guys, sometimes the little man has to take drastic action. Jim Gillespie tells the story of his personal protest.

"In July of 1956, I loaded up our yarder at Cowichan Lake, hauled it to Victoria and put it in front of the Legislative Buildings. It was my way of protesting the awarding of Tree Farm Licence #22 to British Columbia Forest Products Ltd. 14 months earlier. As you know, bribery was involved in the granting of this very valuable licence and the Forests Minister who issued it ended up in jail.

"At the time BCFP applied for that licence, I was a market logger at Cowichan Lake and, like you, Joe, we were buying patches of E & N Railway land grant timber and selling to the local mills, including BCFP at Youbou, on Cowichan Lake.

"BCFP came to me at my little camp. They needed the support of the local loggers for their application. I was only 26 years old, just getting started with a new Murdie 75 gas donkey and a logging truck that didn't have brakes. In those days, many of the logging trucks ran that way. You just learned to steer well and back up fast. There was no such thing as weigh scales. The safety factor was pretty loose. Those trucks carried almost as much on the highway as the big rigs do today, yet ours only had two-ton rear axles.

"Harry Hobson, who was the general manager of the Youbou district for BCFP said, 'Jim, I'd like you to support our application for a Tree Farm Licence.'

"So far these licences haven't proved very good for the smaller loggers," I said.

"'You don't have to worry,' Harry assured me. 'There's plenty there for all of us. As long as we're in business, you're in business. Just sign here.'

"Well," I said, "Sammy Craig up there in the Tofino area is protesting it."

"'Yeah', he went on, 'You don't have to feel sorry about Sammy. There's 20 million feet being signed over to him this week in Victoria by our president Hector Munroe.'

"I took them at their word. I believed I'd have access to timber as an independent logger and signed the paper, saying I had no objections. That was the day before BCFP went before Cabinet.

"A year later, when we had finished our logging above the north arm of Cowichan Lake, I went to see Hobson. When I asked him about moving into the promised logging area, his answer was, "Why don't you go over and talk to Hector Munroe? He has the final say."

"Instead I went down to see Bob Sommers, the Forests Minister.

"'Have you seen Munroe?' Sommers asked.

"No."

"'Well, go and see him. Tell him I sent you.'

"I got the plane to Vancouver right away and went up to the BCFP office. I told the receptionist that Sommers had advised me to get in touch with Mr. Munroe. I got an appointment to meet with him next morning.

"'What can we do for you?' he asked when we met.

"I need timber. Two million feet a year at market prices on a first refusal basis," was my reply. After all, I had been promised timber forever if I signed in favour of their management application.

"'Look, go back and talk to Tom Fraser.'

"Fraser was BCFP's logging manager for the Cowichan District. I was getting very suspicious. Something seemed wrong.

"I met Fraser near their Caycuse camp. The locked gates were opened by a security officer. It was apparent they didn't want anyone else around. It was there that Hobson, the general manager who I had signed on with, joined us. We drove on into the timber.

"The spar tree was already marked with a big X cut into the bark, I couldn't believe it. There was over 100 thousand board feet to the acre, with the longest yarding less than a thousand feet.

"'How much per thousand do you need to log it?' Hobson asked, and then it became clear. This was a different deal.

"What you're trying to do is change me to a flat rate contractor from an independent logger," I snapped, and I told him where they could stuff their timber and contract. That was the final straw. Instead of taking my equipment and logging on their terms, I took it down to Victoria to protest this double-cross.

"It cost me just about all the money I had to hire a lowbed and truck and make banners to explain my position. The Island Highway south of Duncan was under construction, so we had to go around by Cowichan Bay. It was raining, and the road was so slippery that we had to put our jeep on in front of that old Leyland truck and lowbed to get the heavy load up the steep hill past Ordano's boat works. It was another slow grind up the Malahat and on into Victoria.

"It was 3 a.m. before we lined it up directly in front of the Legislature on the north side of Bellevue Street. The lowbed was owned by Evans, Coleman, Johnson Ltd. A guy named Webb was the driver. We had promised him $25 extra if he behaved himself. Since 'Boss' Johnson had been Liberal premier prior to W.A.C. Bennett's Social Credit government, it didn't look good to have the Evans, Coleman, Johnson name involved in a protest right there for everyone to see. That name Johnson would be like a red flag in front of a bull.

"Our problem now was to get the Murdie 75 off the lowbed. There were no trees or stumps to hook on to, so I had to do some fast thinking. I phoned Tom Blackwood, who owned the Victoria

Jim Gillespie's Murdie 75 donkey taken to Victoria as a protest.

Jim giving instructions to the crane operator.

Pile Driving Company and got him out of bed. I told him we needed the biggest crane he had.

"We have a load over here that's shifted," I explained. "I'd pay cash if you could get that crane over by the Legislature before eight o'clock.

"Only a couple of blocks down the street where he was driving piling to repair a wharf, Tom had a 35-ton crane. That was big for those days, and it had to be driven right down Douglas Street. I told the crew a crane was on the way. I didn't want them leaving because our Murdie 75 made a heavy and awkward load.

"The minute the Legislature doors opened, I barged in to see the commissioner and asked, 'Do you mind if we come into the parking lot with a truck? We have to shift a load with a crane.'

"'Just go ahead,' he said. He didn't really know what was happening.

"In those days you could drive right up in front of the buildings and find empty spaces for public parking. The sign didn't say they were for cars only. I checked with our lawyer, who advised that as long as we didn't do any damage they couldn't charge us with trespassing. He said they'd have to get a court order to move us. Our lawyer came down and sat under a tree to watch the proceedings.

"It could never happen again. It was split-second timing. The crane came up, parked in front of the buildings and raised its boom. The lowbed drove under it. We lifted the back end of the donkey sled and heeled it right up in the air. The lowbed moved ahead, the crane now lowered the Murdie 75 so it sat on the pavement exactly where it said 'Public Parking'. I then gave the driver Webb his bonus and suggested he take off. He drove straight through the parking lot, past Premier Bennett's office and out the other end.

"As luck would have it, the back end of the donkey sled had come down right on the white line that marked the end of the public parking area.

64

"'You can take off now. We're finished,' I shouted to the crane operator. When he realized he'd been part of a public protest he wasted no time getting himself and the crane out of there.

"After putting up my protest banners, I stood alone with my briefcase. But in no time at all, a lot of people had gathered around. There were some tourists but mostly civil servants. Word must have spread like wildfire through the government offices. They gathered around the yarder, with all the rigging on it and the banners stating how badly the government was treating small loggers. Across the street, it looked as if the Empress Hotel was being evacuated. People were coming out of every door to see what was going on.

"The Attorney-General's boys phoned both the city police and the Mounties. They came from all directions. I'll never forget the Chief of Police, John Blackstock, waddling along like a mallard duck. He ordered his second-in-command to organize the men and clear the demonstration out.

"I said to him. 'This thing is hot. This is a political matter and you're not supposed to be interfering with politics.'

"What I needed was time, so I had to keep stalling. Soon there were cameras from all over. As I walked around the machine, I talked to the police. It took 14 introductions because there were 14 police. I addressed each one very politely: 'What is your name sir?'

"'Oh, Constable Jones.'

"'Very pleased to meet you, constable.'

"I did that with each one, then came back to the Victoria police chief, who was watching me intently.

"'What's your name, sir?'

"'You know who I am.'

"'No, I don't. I've never seen you before. It's only right that we introduce ourselves in this situation.'

"'I'm Chief Blackstock,' he growled.

"'Very pleased to meet you. I'm Jim Gillespie from Lake Cowichan. By the way, Mr. Blackstock, there's one thing we do

Gillespie discussing procedure with Chief
Blackstock.

Donkey engine in place beneath Premier's office windows.

not want here today. We don't need any of your strong-arm tactics.'

"'No. There'll be none of that, but it's illegal for you to be here with that machine.'

"'No, it isn't. That's where you're wrong, sir. Come back here,' and I led him to the rear of the sled and the crowd followed. The rear snipe of that sled was right on the white line. Pointing to the line, I said, 'We're right on the spot where it says, "Parking".'

"There was a little voice from the crowd: 'That's right. He's on the line.' You could hear the laughter.

"I took out a copy of the Tree Farm Licence and showed the chief Clause 28, which said that 30 percent of the cut was supposed to be done by contract loggers. I pointed out that it did not state any terms.

"'That's what I'm protesting here—"No terms". That's why I loaded the donkey engine and brought it here instead of putting it logging on their Management Licence at a ridiculously low price.'

"Four hours later, after the news media had been briefed and hundreds of pictures taken, Attorney-General Robert Bonner arrived with a dozen of his top officials. W.A.C. Bennett was the Premier, and he'd phoned the police to order the lowbed and crane back to remove the donkey. Everyone was shaken up and nervous. They brought the lowbed back but it sat there idling for over an hour.

"The Murdie donkey was my private property and legally they could not remove it without a court order or on my personal authority. It didn't bother me. I just sat there being interviewed by the press.

"I'd arranged it so Wacky Bennett could see the heavy canvas banners on the fairleads which had been welded to hold their weight. It had cost extra money to have little wind holes cut in them so they wouldn't be blown out of shape. I was prepared for almost everything. The police kept telling us we had to move and I'd say, 'We can't. We've got no stumps. There's no tail-holts here.' I kept them guessing. They didn't know the logging language I was talking.

"I had struggled so hard to get a start, and to think my little company could be forced out of business through broken promises. However, I decided we had made our point and I felt the protest would make the front page in all the newspapers, so I got Blackwood to bring the crane back. There they were, the crane and the lowbed idling away.

"Finally, I went to the Evans, Coleman, Johnson manager and said, 'I'll tell you what I'll do, I'll make you a deal. If you allow me to store this yarder free of charge in your brickyards for any given length of time, and put it in writing, then we'll put this yarder onto the lowbed and leave. But not until then.' The manager pulled out his notebook and scribbled, 'Evans, Coleman, Johnson states the Gillespie yarder can hereby stay in our brickyard for as long as they wish, free of charge.' Then he signed it.

"Within minutes the yarder was loaded and we drove slowly out of the parking lot and right through the middle of town with that overwidth load, its banners flying on both sides.

"We didn't damage a thing. That yarder went through, missing the big cement flower pots on the causeway railings by inches. And my protest was over—but did I win?

"Stan Harrison, a logger in Port Renfrew, phoned me the following week, saying, 'You know, Jim, if it wasn't for that protest I wouldn't be logging. They offered me a good contract to log for five years. After you put that yarder there, they called me up that same day. The next morning, in their Vancouver office, I was told by a BCFP vice-president, 'Stan, we need you. We'll look after you. Nice contract and steady work.'"

"Stan sent me his cheque for $250 to help pay part of the moving expenses. Another logger, Ralph Libel at Cowichan Lake gave me a cheque for $150. I would be reminded about this protest in some of the bunkhouses where I worked years later.

"It was not easy for me to get a job in the woods after that incident in Victoria. I ended up working for H. Winner Construction, a rock-drilling outfit in Victoria. It was something that couldn't be given away by a Tree Farm Licence, and I'll be darned if I didn't end up marrying the owner's daughter.

"So even if I lost my protest, I won a wife and helped some other small loggers!

CHAPTER FIVE

Felled by the Big Guys

Almost a year before Jim Gillespie's trek to the Parliament Buildings in Victoria, there was another independent, gyppo logger struggling to protect himself and others from the timber-hungry large companies. Sammy Craig has his own story to tell.

During the Second World War, Sammy Craig was working at the Mount Sicker Copper Mines on Vancouver Island installing new timbers to shore up the tunnels to prevent falling rock. He was living in Duncan and driving to the mountain's top in an old Chevy he had bought for $75. When this old car could no longer make it up the twisting steep grades, Sammy told the foreman he would have to quit. That was when he found out he was frozen to his job and could not quit because of the importance of copper to the war effort. This copper was needed for the manufacture of ammunition. So Sammy and his family had to move up to the isolated mining camp at the top of Mount Sicker and live in one of the shacks built for married men.

When the war ended, the mine closed down. Back in Duncan with no job and only three dollars in his pocket, he wandered into the Commercial Hotel for a beer. An old friend who was working in a logging camp at Cowichan Lake waved him to his table.

"Could you get me a job?" was Sammy's first question. "I'm out of work and out of money."

"I'll let you know tomorrow."

The following evening, his friend told him there was a booming job open.

"What's a boom?" Sammy asked.

"I'll take you there in the morning and you can find out for yourself. You'll need a pair of good caulked boots."

It snowed about six inches that night and when his friend introduced him to the foreman, Sammy was handed a broom and shovel, and told, "We can't work on the logs today, but go out and clean the snow off the floats."

By the time this was finished it had started to pour with rain, so Sammy went back to the boom shack.

"There's not much we can do until the snow melts off the logs," he was told.

After lunch it warmed up, and the foreman said they'd go and tighten up one of the standing booms. He handed Sammy a pike pole and a sack of cedar plugs. The foreman picked up a heavy boom chain, threw it over his shoulder and with his own pike pole, headed out toward the piling, 500 feet offshore. In disbelief, Sammy watched this big man striding down the single string of boom sticks as they bobbed and rolled under his weight.

"I knew I had to follow and I had never been so scared in my life. How I made it out and back without falling in that freezing water is a mystery," but being nimble as a cat on his feet and weighing only slightly over 100 pounds is what saved Sammy from an icy bath.

Sammy learned quickly and worked around Camp 6 for a couple of years, living in a floating two-room cabin with his wife and two young children. After fishing the kids out of the water on more than one occasion, and fearing the next tumble might be fatal, they decided it was time to make a move. Freddy Knox was logging at Tofino on the west coast of the island and he offered Sammy the job of looking after his A-frame and doing the booming.

Living in a bigger house on dry land had many advantages and Freddy paid good wages. But with the high cost of food in Tofino, because of everything having to be freighted in, the Craigs were finding it difficult to make ends meet. By now they had three youngsters and another on the way.

One day Sammy told Freddy, "I've been thinking of starting my own small logging deal, beachcombing and so on."

"Anything I can do to help you out, just let me know," Freddy offered. This attitude was typical of those who lived and worked along that isolated coast.

Sammy quit his job next day and immediately started building a small A-frame on a float with the help of one man and a Gilcrest jack. From a local sawmill, he was able to get a two-drum winch, complete with an old car engine, for pulling logs off the beach. The price was $750 and he arranged to pay it off in logs, which suited everybody just fine. He was going to be his own boss at last after working for wages all his life.

He found some old logging blocks and other rigging that had been left in the woods from the war years by a company named Seattle Cedars. They were old and outdated oil blocks, but still in working condition. He also salvaged cable from this old machine. Putting it all together within a week, Sammy was ready to start. Mr. Armstrong, the bank manager, agreed to let him have $500 revolving credit, without which he would have been out of business before he started.

With this minimal equipment, financing, and a one-man crew, Sammy began beachcombing. His first log sales were to Harry McQuillan, who had recently sold his timber company to Mac-Millan Bloedel. He'd come to Tofino to run an outfit up the Inlet. When Sammy asked McQuillan if there were any small patches of timber near the water that could be logged with his A-frame, McQuillan said, "By golly, there's one right here near the mill that you can go to work on." This timber had been felled and cut into log lengths during the war and left lying in the woods.

Sammy and his donkey puncher pulled some piling out of the old government wharf, drove a couple of dolphins to anchor the A-frame, and then started yarding the logs into the water. McQuillan loaned them a dozen boomsticks with chains to contain the floating logs and by the end of the first day they had over 30 logs in a bag boom. Sammy, on his first day, had made three times more money than he had ever made working for wages. This was the way to go, he decided that night.

"On the second day, the fellow running the donkey engine pretty near killed me, so I fired him. Now I had no helper and I was on my own wondering what to do next."

Things had changed around in a hurry.

There was a huge cedar log with a sign on it lying half on the mud flats and half in the woods. It had been used as a channel marker. Could he get it into the water on his own? It was way too big for his machine, so he put a block purchase on it and started to pull it free. Half way out it dug so deep into the mud he had to add a second block. When he finally got this huge log in the water and floating, Sammy was completely exhausted. He was sitting there wondering what came next when McQuillan roared up in his speed boat.

"That's a pretty nice log."

"It should scale out at about 5,000 feet," Sammy suggested.

"You're dreaming," Harry countered, and went to the boat for his scaling stick. When he measured it up and made some obvious deductions, it did scale out at just under 5,000. As they sat there chatting, Harry asked, "When you finish here, how'd you like to take out 10 million up at the head of the bay?"

"I couldn't possibly log that with this small machine." Harry offered him financing for a bigger machine if he wanted to take the job. He'd let Sammy know when things were ready to go. Knowing Sammy had got that log in the water by himself had really impressed McQuillan.

A month went by and nothing more was said. Sammy had hired a two-man crew, and was about finished logging the timber near the mill, so he went to see Harry to find out what was going on.

"Hell, I've been going to tell you. I've been dickering on selling out again," McQuillan said.

"I'm disappointed, but if it's good for you, go for it."

"You're included in the deal. As soon as it's ready, I'll be in touch."

A week later, two well-dressed fellows came down to Sammy's house and introduced themselves as being logging officials with Alaska Pine. They were buying Harry McQuillan's timber and part of the deal was that they were to finance Sammy's company, C & B Logging Ltd., to do some of their logging as Harry had promised. They asked Sammy what he needed for equipment.

"Knox Brothers, where I used to work, have a big A-Frame for sale for $5,000 that I'd like to have. I'd also like to have one of Madill's steel spars."

That was in the early 1950s. Alaska Pine had another camp in the next bay, but because of the isolation they decided to close the whole area down. When Sammy asked about the A-Frame they told him, "If you can't afford to pay for it, just keep using it."

Another local gyppo, Jim Taylor, was also contracting for the same outfit so Sammy suggested, "Look, you've got a camp and cats and I've got a steel spar and an A-Frame, why don't we go in together?"

Sammy had noticed some good timber where the present road comes in from Port Alberni. He and Taylor went down and looked this timber over. Sammy was impressed. Taylor said he wouldn't touch it with a ten-foot pole because of the high percentage of balsam. Sammy couldn't get all that big balsam off his mind, so he made a trip to Vancouver and talked to the top brass of Alaska Pine.

"Can you give me any idea of what the future might be for good balsam logs?"

"What a coincidence you should come in here today and ask that question. We've just got word this morning that balsam is being successfully used as a filler for plywood. It should have a real sound future."

Sammy decided to take the plunge. He immediately applied for and got a timber sale of around 10 million in the Public Working Circle. Soon he was logging. When the first barge was shipped out, the formerly unwanted peeler balsam brought $10 more per thousand than the No.1 hemlock. This made him an unexpected and substantial profit.

Without delay Sammy applied for a second 10 million, where he had selected timber that ran heavy to balsam. Within a week he had heard back from the B.C. Forest Service and was again able to purchase this sale without competition.

When Sammy heard rumours of a Tree Farm Licence being applied for in the area, he put up another sale, for 20 million. Three weeks went by with no reply, not even a receipt for his cheque. He phoned the chief forester in Vancouver who informed him, "We'll get back to you within a few days and let you know what's happening."

Sure enough, a registered letter came stating that, because of an application for a Tree Farm Licence in the Clayoquot area by British Columbia Forest Products Ltd., his timber sale application was refused.

Sammy again phoned the chief forester: "What's going on out here? The sale you just turned down is entirely within our Public Working Circle."

Somehow the government had been persuaded, apparently by BCFP, to include all that working circle timber in their Tree Farm Licence. Sammy realized that if he didn't get the 20 million he had applied for, he could be out of timber and out of business within two years. Something strange was going on, and he wanted to find out what.

He went to Vancouver to see Mort Richmond whom he had known as a mining engineer. In the meantime, Mort had married into a lumber family with substantial timber holdings in the Queen Charlotte Islands and had become active in the timber industry with B.C. Forest Products.

After Sammy explained what was happening, Mort just shrugged his shoulders and replied, "Well, that's the way things are and there's nothing I can do for you."

"Mort, I didn't get this far in the logging business without a fight, and by God I'm not going to quit now."

"Well, I'm afraid I can't help you. Go to the top, the government."

From there, Sammy went straight to Victoria to see Dr. Orchard, who was then the Deputy Minister of Forests. He was sympathetic.

"There's no doubt in my mind that you have an absolute right to timber in that working circle. There's no reason why you should not get the timber you have applied for."

"Well, when I went to B.C. Forest Products, Mort Richmond said he could do nothing for me and sent me to you. Now I'm going back and forth from Vancouver to Victoria, and I'm getting pretty fed up with this buck passing."

"There really isn't a great deal I can do for you, Sam," and he walked across the room, pulled down a map and pointed to a fairly large timber lease in the same area where Sammy was logging. It was a lease that had reverted to the Crown.

"That's cruised at something like five million feet, but I'm sure you'll get considerably more than that when you log it. I'm willing to put this timber up as a sale for you. How will that be?"

"Well, that's fine, but there's nothing to say I'll get it. Because of all the publicity we've been getting, people from Port Alberni will likely bid against me."

"Who do you think is likely to bid against you?" he asked.

"MacMillan Bloedel, B.C. Forest Products and maybe others."

"Well," Orchard said, "I can assure you of one thing, neither one of those two big outfits will be bidding against you."

"If I do get it, how about the 20 million I applied for?"

"For what it's worth, you can tell Mr. Richmond that I think you have a right to that timber," Sam was told.

"Can I quote you on that?"

"You can quote me," Dr. Orchard assured him.

Sammy thanked the deputy minister and caught the next plane back to Vancouver. He went directly to Mort Richmond's office.

"Dr. Orchard has been kind enough to give me a little five-million timber lease to tide me over. And he also says I've got a perfect right to the 20 million board feet of timber I applied for, and that I could quote him on that."

"Good for him," Mort said. "Well, I'll tell you something Sam, if you've got timber from Dr. Orchard you're extremely lucky, and I would advise you to be satisfied."

Sammy said in disbelief, "Mort, what sort of people are you working with? That sounds like a threat. I'm going to tell you something. Nothing on God's green earth will stop me from going after the timber we've already applied for."

"Good luck, man," he said, and pointed to the door.

Sammy, mad and determined, kept talking to government officials and writing letters until he found out from his lawyer that his company had the right to go before Cabinet.

A few days before they were to go before Cabinet, his last resort, his lawyer called. "Sammy, we've looked at all the legal aspects and found nothing favourable that might block the Tree Farm Application. It's that damn petition of Schultz', supporting the application that's killing us. Charlie Schultz' consulting company is preparing the application papers for the Tree Farm Licence, and he's doing everything possible to push it through."

Everyone knew C.D. Schultz had clout!

The petition he was referring to had been presented at a special Chamber of Commerce meeting at Ucluelet. A representative from Schultz' company explained that BCFP was applying for a Tree Farm Licence. The meeting was also informed that if they got this timber they would extend the road from Port Alberni out to Tofino and Ucluelet. This was an extremely clever manoeuver. All the people at the meeting had signed because they'd been lobbying the government for a road over the mountain range for over 20 years. It had also been supported at a Parent Teacher Association meeting. But with only a small number of people present at the two meetings, many of the loggers, fishermen, as well as other residents had not been in on the road bribe.

Things were looking pretty hopeless as Sammy sat with his lawyer in Vancouver the following evening when it hit him, "What if we could get a bigger and better petition?"

"If you did," his lawyer said, "that could do it."

"O.K. I'll get back to Tofino and get to work on it."

77

Sammy and Arlene Craig with their family after the move to Tofino.

Right: Sammy with his friend John Blackstock.

Sammy wasted no time in rounding up his crew and explaining the plan. "You fellows have all been working for me for quite some time and have been treated pretty fairly. We're now fighting for our jobs and our homes. I need every one of you to give a hand, because I cannot do it alone. What we must do is go house to house with a petition supporting our timber sale applications. The papers will be printed up tonight and ready for tomorrow morning. All you have to do is explain the petition and get signatures. The petition will read:

> We, the undersigned citizens of the Ucluelet and Tofino areas, hereby support the protest of C & B Logging Co. Ltd. against the application for a Tree Farm Licence by British Columbia Forest Products Ltd. We protest the application where it affects Timber Sale applications of C & B Logging Co. Ltd. not the Tree Farm Licence in general.

"One of the first things people will ask is, 'Will this lose us the promised road from Port Alberni?' Tell them it certainly will not. That's why we are not protesting the licence itself, only the licence as it affects our timber sales and, therefore, our ability to keep on living here and employing people."

Almost everyone they called on signed. It was much bigger in numbers and more representative than the one B.C. Forest Products had, so Sammy decided to go ahead and present their case to Cabinet.

When John Blackstock, manager of the Tahsis Lumber Mill at Port Alberni, read the petition and saw all the signatures, he encouraged Sammy to keep fighting. Sammy had been supplying him with timber at a good price.

Sammy headed off to Victoria armed with the petition and other documents. He told his wife Arlene that he would be staying at the Douglas Hotel. He just wanted to be quiet and plan for his presentation. When Blackstock phoned Arlene, she refused to tell him where her husband was staying.

"God's sake, Arlene, tell me because I need to get to him real quick. It's important as hell."

Unfortunately, Arlene weakened and told him Sammy was at the Douglas Hotel. Shortly after five that evening Blackstock phoned Sammy, saying, "I had a call from BCFP and their president, Hector Munroe, wants to meet with you tonight. He's waiting at the Empress Hotel."

"It's pretty late in the day now, John, to be talking. We've got a meeting with Premier Bennett and his Cabinet tomorrow at ten o'clock."

"All I can say, Sammy, is that it doesn't cost anything to talk. They wouldn't tell me what it's about, just that they are most anxious to talk to you. I'm not involved, but, as your friend, I believe it could be to your advantage to meet with them."

"Okay John. I'll give them a call."

When Sammy phoned, Munroe answered: "It's nice to talk to you, Mr. Craig. I've been away and I would like you to meet with me at seven this evening so we can discuss the situation we find ourselves in. By the way, Tom Fraser, an old friend of yours, is here."

"O.K. I'll be there," replied Sammy, fondly remembering the winter when he worked in the Youbou sawmill and Fraser was the superintendent of logging. Sammy had no dry wood in his wet floating shack and Fraser had a truck load of kiln-dried plane trimmings delivered. From that experience began a lasting friendship. Later, Sammy was to wonder if Munroe, knowing of this friendship, had brought Fraser in as bait. Certainly when Sammy shook hands and remembered those early days he relaxed and felt less threatened.

At the hotel, Tom Fraser opened the door with a big grin and a handshake, then introduced him to the lawyer for BCFP and the president Hector Munroe, who, speaking apologetically, immediately started negotiations.

"First, let me say that it's too bad I've been away ill, because this is the most ridiculous thing I've ever been involved in. It stands to reason you have rights to some of that Clayoquot timber, and we are the ones in the wrong. You were in that Public Working Circle doing what you're supposed to be doing. We came along and tried to push you out. It's as simple as that. What I would like to do is rectify this in any way I can. I know it's late, but whatever it takes to make it right, we are willing to do."

Sammy didn't know what to say.

"This fight has been going on for a considerable time. Now, all of a sudden, everything changes. You realize I've applied to go before Cabinet in the morning with my petition and I can't see them turning me down."

Munroe agreed: "I don't think they will turn you down, but this is a bad deal for us. We've already had bad publicity over Mr. Sommers and those many long months of newspaper stories, and now we could have more over this. I'm desperately trying to avoid any further problems. Even if you do win, Mr. Craig, they're not likely to refuse our Tree Farm Licence, so you'll have to deal with us later on in any event. It's a case of do we deal as friends or do we deal as enemies? I don't expect you to give us an immediate answer, but could you think it over for an hour or two?"

"I'll have to, Mr. Munroe."

"Can you give us an answer by nine o'clock?" Munroe asked. "We have to know."

"I'll phone you."

"One thing, Sam. In all fairness, I've got to tell you that if you proceed tomorrow to present your petition, I have instructed our lawyer to immediately stand and advise Mr. Bennett and his Cabinet that we have discussed with you all your objections and have offered to meet every one of them. We don't like to do this, but we've no choice. You know Mr. Bennett. He's likely to just say, 'Thank you, Mr. Craig, we're glad you've been looked after. Good-day'."

Sammy walked over and sat on the steps of the Legislative Buildings to consider B.C. Forest Product's offer. He would be able to log the three timber sales he already had. If he protested, he was almost sure to win the additional 20 million that had been refused, but it was evident BCFP was going to do everything possible to prevent him from presenting his petition and having it made public. Sammy felt quite sure that BCFP would follow through with what they had promised, because his friend Tom Fraser was there and he would insist on it.

As he sat on the steps alone, Sammy realized he had been tricked. Munroe had cleverly made it impossible for him to present the petition he had worked so hard to obtain. He had been told exactly what was going to happen if he tried to present either objection, or the petition. He realized he had made a grave mistake going to Munroe's room to talk. He had been relaxed and unsuspecting in the presence of his friend Tom Fraser. He stood up and walked slowly back to his room at the Douglas Hotel.

Next morning, in front of the Premier and his Social Credit Cabinet, the BCFP lawyer stood and declared there'd been a meeting and all Sammy Craig's objections had been satisfied. The *Victoria Times*, on May 27, 1955, reported the following:

> Mr. Gibson says that B.C. Forest Products, by a hotel room deal, persuaded logger Sammy Craig not to appeal against its application for the Clayoquot district licence by assuring him cutting rights on 26,000,000 feet of timber for which he would receive the open market price. By Mr. Gibson's figuring that "deal was worth a minimum of $125,000 to Mr. Craig over and above his normal profit...."
>
> "The danger lies in the fact that his action has been construed by those who cancelled this public working circle...as being a quit claim by every British Columbia citizen of this and future generations to the timber stand which was theirs since the British Crown acquired it on their behalf at Nootka in 1875."

Years later, Sammy threatened to sue Gordon Gibson for $100,000 because he had included the above newspaper excerpt in the first edition of the book, *Bull of the Woods*. Sammy considered the newspaper article slanderous, but, when Gibson apologized and agreed to have the article deleted from all future printings, Sammy dropped the suit. Another possible reason for not suing could have been that Gibson would probably fight the case through to the Supreme Court of Canada with the help and advice of his Vancouver publisher. Sammy and his lawyer believed they would probably win the case and get damages of between $20,000 and $30,000. However, the cost of getting to the Supreme Court could be in excess of $50,000.

It wasn't long after the appearance before Cabinet that BCFP president Munroe died. The police talked to Sammy about Munroe's death. Sammy felt it was probably a combination of two things: pressure and poor health. Munroe's company, BCFP, was in serious trouble over the Sommers bribery affair, and his health had reportedly been poor for some time.

"He certainly looked well when I saw him at the hotel," Sammy remembers. "Yet it was only a matter of days and he was dead. It happened just after the police had arrested Sommers and advised Mr. Munroe that he would also have to be arrested and face bribery charges."

Sammy said the police told him that suicide had not been ruled out. The cause of his sudden and untimely death was never disclosed to the public.

Anyway, Munroe's hotel room deal that BCFP would meet all Sammy's objections only lasted for a couple of years. Sammy was asked to submit a bid to log some of BCFP's west coast timber at a contract price. Under government regulations at that time, Tree Farm Licence holders had to contract out between 30 and 50 percent of their logging to smaller operators.

"What's to stop other loggers who have nothing to lose from putting in a ridiculously low price?" Sammy wanted to know.

"We'll agree that anybody bidding within $2 a thousand under your bid will not be considered," he was told. Sammy really had no choice if he wanted to keep on logging, so he submitted a bid. That was the middle of November.

He clearly remembers, "Only two days before Christmas I got a registered letter. It said my bid had been refused. They'd given the contract to someone whose offer was 50 cents a thousand less than mine! I couldn't believe that people in the timber business would break their word so soon after giving their promise. As you must well remember, in those days a handshake was as good as a signed document."

That is the way Sammy Craig related to me his struggle to try and save the Clayoquot Public Working Circle during our interview in Tofino on March 30, 1991.

In trying to stop B.C. Forest Products, Sammy was also trying to protect his own right to acquire timber. Like many others, he felt the small contractor had to speak up against multinational corporations and government meddling.

His biggest mistake was in stepping through that hotel room door alone, where he was outmaneuvered and trapped. He believes to this day that if he had stayed quietly in his own hotel room that evening, as originally planned, B.C. Forest Products might never have been issued a licence that included the Clayoquot Public Working Circle. Twenty-five years later, Sammy Craig is living in a mobile home in Tofino. He is old, on oxygen most of the time, and broke; and the forest companies are prospering and powerful.

In the British Columbia woods, many a sapling, such as Sammy, has been chopped down to make room for the bigger trees. But no matter how noble and dignified these timber giants appear, some of them are rotten to the core.

CHAPTER SIX

Changing with the Times

Coulson Forest Products Limited is a long established and reputable coastal logging company, well respected by the B.C. Forest Service and the citizens of Port Alberni. The company has logged for over 40 years, and is the largest small and family-controlled forest company in British Columbia. Coulson's is the type of company which tends to fall "between the cracks" in the public's comprehension of what forestry is all about because the giant organizations dominate the politics of the industry and the financial pages. But each is vitally important to local communities.

I interviewed Cliff at his Port Alberni head office and he told of one interesting little episode he had to deal with while his company was contract logging that illustrates there is more to being a logger than just taking out timber.

They were logging on Tree Farm Licence #44 at the Sproat Lake Division for MacMillan Bloedel when Cliff was approached by the local M&B manager who ordered, "You'll have to change your oil and fuel account. We've made a deal with Shell Oil to supply all our fuel needs for this logging division."

"I don't intend to change from the company that has been looking after us for the past 20 years," said Cliff, a no-nonsense guy who has survived in good, bad and worse times.

"We hold the management licence," was the response. "We reserve the right to say who comes on it and who does our logging."

As far as MacMillan Bloedel was concerned, that was that, and Coulson, the sub-contractor would toe the line or else.

"We'll try that one on for size in the courts," Cliff answered. "I reserve the right to run my own business and buy from suppliers of my choice." And he walked to his pickup which was loaded with four barrels of Chevron diesel.

That afternoon, playing tough guy, the M&B manager gave Cliff an ultimatum: "It's either Shell, or we can't use you."

"Well, let's go to court and see," Cliff snapped back.

Cliff went to the Chevron wholesale dealer in Port Alberni and briefed the manager, stating, "You guys are in this with me. If I run out of money you'd better be there."

The manager, after a phone call to his Vancouver head office, agreed to join the Coulsons in the fight. They won. Having tried it on for size, the big company had to back off, something they definitely are not used to doing.

"The point of this little story is to remind us that some big companies holding Tree Farm Licences believe they can get away with almost anything," Cliff declared. "They have been used to playing God for too long."

Okay, but who is Cliff Coulson? If you're looking at small independent logging on Vancouver Island, he's a good starting point. He's 72, and still in the office at seven a.m. He comes in on Saturdays too, puts on the coffee for anyone who drops by and answers the phone to keep the show going.

In 1934, during the Depression, he went into the woods as a chokerman. War came and he served five and a half years overseas. Although logging was essential to the war effort and he could have ducked, he didn't. Returning home as a sergeant, he worked for wages until '48, when he got the urge to get out on his own. His first pieces of equipment were an old Cat, an arch and a lowbed truck, and he worked as a contractor wherever there was work. He laughed as he said, "You made it where you could and sometimes it was tough. I mean tough.

"I always paid the bills, bought the groceries and what was left was mine. Not much sometimes."

Up and down times, he had them, "but I never went broke."

Cliff worked many long hours to build up and expand his logging outfit. "We're not big, but we've stayed in this valley and it is still a family business. We've done what we could for the town through thick and thin, and the town has been good to us."

Coulson Forest Products Ltd. is a private company with three sons and one daughter working as partners with Cliff. "We're all in this together and unless the kids decide to go public, we won't."

I asked him, "Are you union?"

"You bet, IWA Local 185. We have our differences but we get along well. I believe in the union. Treat them right and they'll treat you right. If you have problems, fill up the coffee cups and sit around and talk it out. It works."

That's Cliff Coulson, son of a logger, father of loggers, a little guy by MacMillan Bloedel standards, but they keep about 90 on the payroll even in bad times.

"How much timber do you have in this area?" I asked.

"At present, we have the Toquart Valley as one timber area. There's about 14 years of logging left in there on our present quota of 55,000 cubic meters a year." Cliff explained, "5,000 cubic meters equals approximately one million board feet on the old B.C. log scale. So we're taking out a lot of wood.

"Our two new applications are for major timber sales under the Small Business Program. AC Mokko Manufacturing Limited is a new company formed by my son Wayne, who is the principal owner. It is his initiative that has led us to this bid proposal. It's his show, win or loose. These are Category II sales with a quota of two million cubic meters and an annual allowable cut of one million from each sale over a ten-year term. During this time, we must either build or have a definite arrangement with some manufacturing plant that can remanufacture this timber into value-added products. We just cannot cut and haul anymore. The whole thing has changed.

"One of the sale areas is exclusively helicopter logging on some very steep mountain slopes. This sale, A33539, which was originally part of Tree Farm Licence #19, is one of the new 5 percent government takebacks from the larger Tree Farm Licence holders. A good policy. It keeps the little guys alive, more jobs, more profits. We hope. It was controlled by Canadian Pacific Forest Products. They're not in the helicopter logging business and apparently don't want to be. Our helicopter show up above the McCurdy Creek Valley has already been logged out in the lower accessible areas where trucks could be used. But higher up on those mountains is a large volume of high grade yellow cedar, hemlock and balsam. In other words, the lower area had been creamed. The easy timber is all taken out, and the big companies don't want to bother with the higher, tougher stuff. But we do.

"Our other sale, A34814, is in the Arrowsmith Timber Sale Area and is suited for conventional logging. Roads, trucks; no big deal when you know how."

"Is that 5 percent takeback going to be enforced and carried on?" I asked. "Or will the government change policy again?"

"I've been told it will, and it could possibly even be increased to 10 percent in the near future. The Truck Loggers Association, comprised of us small companies, is recommending a 50 percent takeback," Cliff added.

"When the recession of the early '80s came, we were unable to sell our logs locally or on the open market. We had to have export permits to sell the logs to Japan. We recognized then that we would have to get into manufacturing if we were going to stay in business. If we couldn't sell our logs to the big boys, we would soon lose our annual allowable cut."

Coulson explained. "You remember the hearing, Joe, when government agreed we needed security of tenure, the promise we'd always get logs to cut, haul and sell, in order to maintain the timber towns and lumber communities. It was agreed that modern manufacturing plants plus sufficient timber could maintain these established districts for the long term."

"I don't know if you remember, Joe, but we went down to the Legislative Buildings in Victoria and put on a big demonstration. That was in 1982. We were being refused export permits and we explained that we either had to get these permits or shut down. It was that bad.

"Jack Heinrich was the Forests Minister at the time. In desperation, we got all the independent loggers from the Alberni district together and loaded a bunch of logging equipment on lowbeds and logging trucks. We then drove to Victoria and parked our unwieldy caravan. But it was more than a publicity stunt for television news. After several hours of discussion, Heinrich just had to back down. He reluctantly gave us the export permits. Without them, all of the gyppo loggers in the Alberni district would have been forced to close down, causing the immediate loss of several hundred jobs.

"The multinationals, M&B, BCFP, the lot of them, holding management licences and paying lower stumpage because of the lousy markets, didn't need our logs. It was just as simple as that. Premier Bill Bennett certainly didn't give us any sympathy. He couldn't seem to understand that we either had to export or go broke. He's a smart businessman, yet he just couldn't understand. I still don't understand his attitude," Cliff admitted.

"Is it any wonder, Cliff, that our forest industry is in trouble with such political stupidity?" I asked. "You fly over this area all the time, Cliff, on your way out to your logging operations. What is your opinion of the present reforestation effort?"

"Most of the licensees holding tree farms seem to be doing a pretty good job of reforesting lately. Because of the pressure being put on them they have improved. Some of the older government timber sales are poorly re-stocked. In those days, reforestation was not considered necessary. Most of the money we paid as stumpage went straight into general revenue, not to improve the forests. There are timber sale areas that we logged here 30 years ago that have never been replanted. It wasn't part of our logging contract then. Things have come a long way recently. Pressure by environmentalists and the general public are demanding better forestry practices.

"There's talk that within 20 years the provincial annual allowable cut could be reduced again by as much as 20 percent or more. It's going to be a real problem unless we get into value-added products, such as moldings, windows, doors, cupboards and furniture, and create more jobs and more timber.

"In Japan, there's hundreds of little mom-and-pop type factories. When the mills are cutting logs into lumber and timbers, these people collect the edgings and slabs and take them to their homes where they operate little factories and make value-added products out of the wood we Canadians are now wasting. They're great on finger-jointing and glueing. All their houses are built up two or three stories, so there are a lot of stair treads in Japan. They're using these little short pieces of wood, glueing them together, matching the colour, sanding them, and you can barely see the joints. Most of their stair treads are of finger-jointed wood. It's stronger material because it has no knots and doesn't warp.

"Tree Farm Licence holders can charge almost any expense against their stumpage. The advantage again is for the Big Boys. This is changing to some extent, but certainly there is plenty of room for improvement. Small business sales, like we are in, are usually sold by competitive bidding. Tree Farm Licences are awarded without competition.

"Our stumpage is averaging about $19 a cubic meter under this small business system. In some places, it's slightly lower; others it's a bit higher. **This seems to be about 50 percent more than the big licence holders are paying.** Yet we're responsible for the same expenses as the big companies, such as fire protection, silviculture, replanting and getting the logged areas up to the satisfactory growth height of about five to six feet.

"We have to go in and, if the young trees are getting choked out with weeds or brush, clear around them. We, the little guys, make sure that 90 percent of what we've planted survives. Those that don't survive are replaced. In some places where the brush is heavy, we have to replant with three-year-old seedlings, and that can be very costly. You have to check and double-check every plantation each year.

"It takes five years to satisfy the Forest Service and if you haven't done all the necessary things, your licence deposit is in jeopardy. According to our new contract, the B.C. Ministry of Forests can take what money they need from our deposit to re-plant or do whatever other forestry work they deem necessary.

"The Forests Ministry is starting to get tough on loggers and mills. If you leave usable waste in the woods, rangers come along and scale it and they can claim it to be avoidable waste. The licensee is not only going to pay stumpage for it at double the regular rate, but the volume of this waste wood will be taken off his quota. They've only introduced this in the last year. This is revolutionary. We used to be allowed to leave as much as 35 cubic meters per hectare with no penalty. Now they measure high stumps. If you leave wood more than the allowable number of centimeters on the high side it's also scaled as a penalty. They're getting tougher, but it took a long, long time," Coulson stated.

"Although the Tree Farm Licence holders log about 70 percent of the total annual cut in our province, they pay only 30 percent of the stumpage money that goes into the government coffers. You figure that one out!

"In addition, because of the pressure being put on logging by the environmentalists, we find it expedient to hire our own consultants. Our judgment could be questioned if we didn't. Gordie Atkinson, who worked with Tommy Thomson for several years, advises us on our wildlife habitat and fish-spawning areas. He also helps to supervise our planting and logging layouts. He even finds time on weekends to work with our chief pilot Bob Hawthorne on the helicopter shows.

"Most of the registered professional foresters in our province work for the major companies. There they are, sitting behind a desk in some downtown office instead of being out sweating in the woods where their education and knowledge can do the industry some good," Coulson said, and he grinned.

He also believes that land tenure must be removed from the political arena, where government policy can change with every election. Politics and forest management are a bad mix. Some sort of a Forest Resource Commission should be selected and appointed on a permanent basis to guide the destiny of British Columbia's present and future land resources. After all, these resources are our number one employer and dollar earner.

Such a commission will have to work closely with the government to set and maintain policy, and to supervise the growing of our future crops. Without forest-related jobs, B.C. would be a sorry province. This commission must include professional foresters along with business people, manufacturers, loggers, recreationists and others with a stake in the future of our public lands. Without trees, you've got nothing.

"The Carmanah Valley? What did we do, Joe? Cut it in half. That was political. Trying to please everyone, the government satisfied no one. What's happening in our forests today is much too political. I'm sure the political interference in the South Moresby situation with the environmentalists, the Haida Indians, the politicians, the media, is what drove Frank Beban of Nanaimo to an early grave. Heart attack. They made him out the bad guy, yet he was just the contractor, cutting trees, providing jobs.

"The Arrowsmith area is about the only Timber Sale Area in this forest district that does not seem to have a shortage of timber. The day of the shake-and-shingle business on the West Coast is almost gone. It was good business in its day. Some operators were using small helicopters to get shake cedar out to the roads where it could be loaded on trucks. The two MacKenzie boys have been eight years out here, taking shakes out this way. They use a long nylon rope to haul the shake bundles up and out from the cutting site. They can make money at it when the market's good, but that embargo the U.S.A. slapped on really hurt the shake business. Only the best are able to carry on."

Coulson's chief logging pilot said that the cost of operating their old 61 Sikorsky is about $3,000 per hour, while the 64 Sikorsky, with a third more lifting capacity, costs just under $6,000.

"So, only if you're logging oversized timber can you afford to own the big helicopter, and there's not enough of that left to make it practical. Where we've got a block of oversized timber we go in and take out all the smaller timber first with the 61, then we find it economical to contract-hire a 64 to take out the big stuff."

Wayne Coulson said, "Those helicopter pilots are really something. The S61s can pick up a 5-ton load on the end of its line, and as it comes down the hillside it has to turn to drop the logs in the water or on a landing. This causes the load to really swing out, and when they let it drop, holy smoke! The chopper goes up like it's on the end of a bungy cord."

Wayne explained, "We now need several pilots during the summer months because of the double-shifting. During the hot weather we get special permits to log with the helicopters because we keep our bambi-buckets ready to put out fires at all times. These buckets carry the water. The Forest Service likes to keep us operating because we're there with experienced people and equipment if a fire starts."

"We're a fire-fighting crew as well as a logging crew," Hawthorne explained, "We can usually put out a fire in a matter of minutes. On the steep sidehills like they have near Powell Lake over on the mainland, a fire can roar to the top of those mountains in a very short time. If we are right there we can have the fire out before it gets well started. Last year we put in 230 hours fighting fires in Manitoba. This year we haven't been that busy, but we're on constant standby with both the Canadian and American forestry departments. We can go anywhere, anytime, at a moment's notice.

"Helicopters may be one of the most expensive ways to log, but it's by far the safest when it comes to land damage and fire protection. The B.C. Forest Service now has an appraisal cost manual," Bob Hawthorne explained. "They monitored our times on several fires to get the actual costs. If you have a two-minute fly one way and a four-minute fly the other, they'll allow us a six-minute average for each turn of water dumped on a fire."

"Do you find our Forest Service more cooperative than it used to be?" I asked Cliff.

Vertol 107 helicopter dropping a turn of logs in the saltchuck.

"Yes," he replied without hesitation. "We are now allowed to write-off our fire-fighting costs against our stumpage, which is a great help."

He then handed me a copy of a beautifully laid out proposal for both logging and a high-tech mill; one that has taken a great deal of time and money.

The Coulsons had planned to go partners with a Japanese manufacturing company that has been buying logs from them for several years. That market has now pretty well dried up. The company is in the lumber business in a substantial way in Japan, and would supply state-of-the-art machinery to be installed in the planned manufacturing plant.

When the *Forest Act* changed in 1979, it made it possible to borrow money using a timber sale licence as collateral. This gave the Coulsons the necessary funds to buy the timber for their proposed specialized mill, estimated to cost some $18 million.

When the deal with the Japanese got down to the nitty-gritty months later, and the details and financing were being put in place, the Coulson bunch, independent as ever, began to have second thoughts. Things just weren't right.

They knew the Alberni citizens were happy with the plans for the new mill. But Cliff, who remembered those days with the Cat and the lowbed, began to have doubts. He had trouble dealing with the Japanese. The same language wasn't being spoken.

"We were in the logging and lumbering business here, and they were over there in Tokyo. You'd phone and get the runaround, then they'd come back with new specifications and deals. It went on and on and on. We didn't seem to be getting any closer to a satisfactory agreement. So our family got together and talked it over and decided to go it alone.

"Looking back it was the right decision. We had a good reputation and the government gave us a $2.5 million guarantee. The Royal Bank came through with the same amount. They had confidence in us. I had never missed a payment in over 30 years. Even back in the old days if we were low on funds I would go to the bank manager and let him know we would be a day or two late. I guess they never forgot this.

"We began work on the new mill site in mid-September 1991, and we expect it to be up and running within nine months," Cliff says. "The first phase calls for the processing of logs 18 inches and up."

The Coulson mill is a sophisticated operation that will employ 35 at start-up and then increase to 70 within a year, an important factor in the economy of the valley which has been hard hit by low lumber prices, more taxes, new tariffs and other complications. It will manufacture value-added specialty products, because Coulson, even at 72, knows that progress means staying with the competition and doing everything to edge ahead.

Port Alberni was happy when the Coulson-Japanese deal was announced, but are even more pleased now that they know it will be locally-owned even though the projected number of jobs may be slightly less.

"This town, this valley, has done a lot for our family. Now we want to do the best we can for the town and our employees. What is good for us is good for everyone. I firmly believe that, and so do my kids."

Coulson is also proud of his relations with the local Indians, several of whom he employs. But his involvement with them in Hecate Logging is a high point.

The Ehattesaht Indian Band received cutting rights near Zeballos and, with a government grant, established Ehattesaht Logging, which went broke. Coulson, needing timber, went into partnership with another logger, Earl Smith, a band member. The three partners set up Hecate Logging to cut the timber. The firm employed natives and the band also received enough money for their cutting rights to save their seine boats. The Indian cutting rights are now handled by R.J. Coulson Contracting, a company set up by Coulson's son Ron, and the band receives 50 percent of the benefits.

So there is the Coulson family, the type you rarely hear of in these days of multinationals, yet their annual dollar turnover is

$25 million. You'll see this figure climb as the new mill goes into production. How high? It depends on the Boss and the workers pulling together as one unit.

It would appear Cliff Coulson and his family have not yet used up their capacity for hard work and they certainly have the practical experience to make a success in this new venture. Even more important is the fact that they now have the necessary timber to keep the project going.

This is the type of operation every timber town needs to keep it stable, and this is the type of family that could well be the forest industry's salvation.

CHAPTER SEVEN

Voice of the North

Bob Harkins is one of the down-to-earth breed of people living in and around Prince George, a promoter of his community, with a keen interest in young people, their sports and their environment.

I met Bob when he was the bat boy for our company's baseball team in Duncan on Vancouver Island. This was a small city just 50 miles north of Victoria, but we had an A-class team. Bob will probably remember playing the professional Victoria team. Though they usually beat us, we did manage to come out ahead on several occasions. We were good senior amateurs who played for the fun of it.

When Bob's family moved to Prince George he worked in his dad's sawmill. He helped with the logging which was done with a team of horses. But he didn't like the black flies and mosquitos, so he decided to try something different.

He was one of the prime movers in establishing the first radio station in Prince George and went on to become its manager. Bob became known as "The Voice of the North" and was the most listened-to broadcaster from Williams Lake up north to Fort St. John and as far west as Hazelton, a vast but sparsely settled land. Bob also did considerable writing for the local newspapers and magazines. He is a longtime member of City Council, but was defeated when he ran in the 1988 federal election to represent Prince George in Ottawa. He was a Liberal and the Tories won by an avalanche everywhere.

On a trip north in early November, 1990, I visited Bob in his comfortable home a few miles south of Prince George to get his views on the lumber and pulp industries. After Sunday brunch, I asked Bob, "How well did you know Ray Williston?"

"We worked together on many community projects. In those days, Prince George was rather unsophisticated, with plenty of tarpaper shacks. To me, Ray Williston was one of the greatest conservationists who has ever been part of the British Columbia government.

"It was through the efforts of Williston, Poldi Bentley and John Liersch, co-founders of Canadian Forest Products, Tom Wright, their chief forester, and Ian Mahood who was consulting for them, that the first pulp mill in northern B.C. was built right here in Prince George. It was built in association with an English company, Reed Corporation, who arranged for the machinery. Their plans called for 500 tons of bleached kraft pulp daily. Construction started in 1964 and was completed by the spring of 1966 at a cost of some $80 million, an awful lot of money in those days."

"I know for a fact, Bob, that both Poldi and Ray went out with their foresters and actually measured the circumference of some of the pine trees with a pocket tape," I recalled with a chuckle.

"The pulp mills may have been the last feather in Ray's cap, but will always be one of his biggest," Bob added. "There was never any possibility of underhanded deals while he was Minister of Forests. We were lucky to have had him. You'll be saying in this book all the things that I believe need to be said."

Bob handed me a booklet he had recently completed honouring the first 50 years of the Northern Interior Lumber Sector (NILS). Some excerpts follow:

> Today dense second-growth obscures the remains of many old sawmill settlements straddling the CN tracks out east of Prince George. If you could just look through the trees you would see the remains of many once-vibrant lumber communities. Piles of rotting sawdust, rusting beehive burners, abandoned steam boilers, crumbling stacks of old firebrick and massive concrete foundations that once anchored gangsaws are all that remain of a romantic era that time and technology have passed by.

Three decades ago the sawmills along the rail line east of Prince George went into a slump from which they never recovered. They died of starvation. The old sawmills had run out of the big trees that once grew in the Upper Fraser Valley. All those mills were built for big timber and had to close. The workers and their families drifted away in search of greener pastures. The forest gradually reclaimed its ownership.

"The old sawmills became extinct because they could no longer compete. The new age demanded maximum productivity and efficiency," Bob said.

"Well, Bob, technology has crept up on us. There has been too much needless waste without sufficient and proper reforestation being practised. I know we're going to suffer for it," I remarked. "There's going to be a dead period in the creation of new forests."

"Particularly in the north," Bob agreed. "Northwood Pulp and Timber has closed its last big log mill in the area. They say it was no longer cost-efficient but the truth is, there is little or no big timber left. They've already logged all the river and creek bottoms. Now they're going up the side-hills, and in this country, that's where the small timber is. The new-type mills can handle this smaller material, and that's all they have left to process for the foreseeable future.

"Bob, how long do you think it takes to grow a pine forest in this area, say from the time you plant a two-year old seedling to a usable sized tree, provided it was properly looked after?" I asked.

"I don't know exactly. It depends on the land. If you just leave them alone, you're probably looking at an average of 40 years. However, considering future reforestation," Bob noted, "there are some interesting experiments being carried out at the Prince George Red Rock Nursery about 20 miles south of town. This plantation is located on an exceptionally good growing site west of the highway towards the Fraser River. They're doing a lot of good solid research which is bound to pay off in the years ahead. They are developing some excellent pine trees. They are now

100

producing in excess of 15-million super-seedlings a year. I've been through the plantation and it's exciting to see.

"In less than 15 years they can have these trees capable of producing seed. They are pollinated under controlled conditions. With the type of seedling they're creating they should be able to dramatically shorten the growing period by at least 10 to 15 percent, which would give a full rotation in 35 years. It gives a person some confidence and hope for the future.

"This nursery was taken over from the B.C. Forest Service in the mid-80s by Pacific Regeneration Technology Inc. who have their head office in Victoria. They have nurseries throughout the province that sell seedlings to both industry and the Forest Service.

"Northwood is starting to do a good job of reforestation in this north country, and we should give them full credit. They're experimenting with sheep. They've brought in thousands of them and put them into the logged-off areas. These sheep are being looked after by competent shepherds with good dogs that keep the cougars, wolves and coyotes away. As you know, sheep eat almost anything that's broad-leaf and they also keep the grass and weeds under control. They also do a bit of fertilizing along the way," Bob added. "The shepherds are there to help put out or report forest fires started by lightning, careless campers, or any other way. The young forests are growing better with the help of the sheep."

I asked Bob if he thought that the big operators could do the job of reforestation as well as family-sized operations.

"No, I don't. Right now I'm worried about the control the big companies have. I do a lot of travelling off the main highways in the north where the general public rarely go. I've seen nothing up there to give me any confidence that the big companies are even trying to grow new forests. I don't believe they're paying sufficient attention to the environment. I'm also quite sure they're trying to give the general public a snow job."

"Pretty harsh words," I said.

"Well, Joe, that's now the opinion of Tony Chiappe and Don Gillowland, a couple of old friends who live north of here at Germansen Landing.

"In September, 1990, they held a meeting for the local people to discuss off-highway loads on portions of what was once the Omineca Mines Access Road. Among those present were Rick Hansen of Fletcher Challenge, and Gary Zomber of the B.C. Forest Service for the Mackenzie District.

Bob went on to describe the communication gap between big companies and local people. "To give you a brief background. The road north from Fort St. James has for decades been the only access road for the people living in Manson Creek and Germansen Landing, way back of beyond. For years this road was under the jurisdiction of the Ministry of Mines. Then jurisdiction was transferred to the B.C. Ministry of Highways, which did a great amount of grading and ditching. In the past few years portions of the road have once again been transferred, this time to the B.C. Forest Service, or if you like, the Ministry of Forests. These portions have been designated as forest access roads.

"This shift in jurisdiction has permitted Fletcher Challenge to use their off-highway trucks with bunks 15 feet wide, carrying loads up to 100 tons. Think of it, 100 tons!

"However, in the latter part of 1989 a local Resource Planning Committee was formed composed of Fletcher Challenge, the Mackenzie Forest Service and the residents of Manson Creek and Germansen Landing. There has been little or no progress or cooperation up to now. The residents still insist that those overwidth trucks are dangerous to others on the road. There are sharp corners with little or no visibility, and no radio contact between the private cars and the drivers of those huge trucks. Fletcher Challenge is saying that a 100-ton vehicle with 15 feet wide loads are no more of a hazard than a standard half ton pick-up. They candidly admit that using the off-highway loads improves the profit margin to their shareholders.

"These are some of the conditions the people who live up there must face when they travel over these narrow roads. It's the only road to the outside world. It's just a matter of time before some-one gets killed. But Fletcher Challenge, which is a New Zealand company by the way, does as it pleases. The pioneers and other settlers seem to count for nothing.

"Don Gillowland was one of the earliest settlers. He came to the district during the 1930s. He's been a trapper and a prospector, done some mining and now operates a lodge. He understands the wildlife and knows the impact logging is having on some of the herds of caribou in the Omineca Valley. Few people ever see this country. Tourists would be risking their lives by driving on this road as long as it's being used by the logging trucks.

"The only reason our family goes up there now," Bob said, "is because of our friendship with Tony Chiappe. It makes us sad to see how they're raping the area. Tony visited us here last winter and we got talking about it.

"We decided to convene a big meeting in support of the residents of the Omineca Valley. We invited some Fletcher Challenge big-wigs, Quint Nelson and some of his forestry staff, and Jack Kempf our MLA. I volunteered to act as moderator, representing the "Voice of the North" on radio. Ken Bernsohn agreed to organize the media end of it.

"At first Fletcher Challenge was hesitant to attend, but was more or less forced to be there to protect its public image. The presence of the media was plenty strong. CBC television felt it was important enough to cover. We had a good meeting and some good debates. There were about 150 people present. Jack Kempf gave an excellent speech. He's the only politician who's ever actually gone in there to see and hear what's going on.

"As far as we know, no major action has been taken on their recommendations.

Bob continued, "To give you another example of the power of the big corporations, look at the Nechako River and the Alcan situation. Alcan, the Aluminum Company of Canada, another giant as you probably remember, got the total water rights over all the water systems that run into Kitimat River. They've already destroyed the Nechako River. Now they're going to lower it even more. It's had a damaging effect on the community of Vanderhoof. Though Prince George benefits from the Stewart River, the impact of the reduction in the Nechako will be felt here. Vanderhoof has lost its river and all the benefits that go with it. Remember when the Nechako was a big river? Look at it now.

"An agreement signed with the federal and provincial governments gave Alcan the authority to do this. Any intelligent person will say that the resources of this country, particularly those that emanate from our major river systems, should be administered by something like a Permanent Rivers Commission. That commission could represent the users of all the river systems. That means Alcan would be represented along with the ranchers and recreation people, instead of this one-sided deal by people in Victoria and Ottawa making decisions on things they have never even seen. The local people directly involved must have a voice in such decision-making. But they were never even considered. It seems as though local people don't count.

"The people of Vanderhoof should have a say in how much water comes down the Nechako River, and when. That's important. If there isn't a sufficient flow during the spawning season, all those trout and spawning Pacific salmon will be lost. During a dry year they rarely open the flood gates at Skins Lake because they claim they need all the water for electric power. They say it's the first priority, but I don't believe it should be the only priority.

"Another bad thing is the effect logging is having on the Stoney Creek Indians. Since the clearcut logging has taken place, they have lost practically all of their creeks. The water just runs away like water off a roof during the spring and summer rains. The creeks I remember fishing in there are now dry for most of the year. They were once good-sized streams, full of trout. Now there's nothing. This situation will definitely continue to exist until the new crop of trees reaches a sufficient size to retain some moisture to prevent run-off.

"In this particular part of the north, land can still be preempted for ranching as it was in the old days. You can get 160 acres surveyed and buy it for between $50,000 to $60,000 from the government. In some cases, the ink is barely dry on the land deed before these so-called homesteaders are clearcutting. The value received for the logs will be somewhere around $300,000. The so-called ranchers can then decide they no longer want to be ranchers and let the land revert to the government for taxes. Because it was private land, they did not have to abide by normal forestry regulations. This scam must be stopped. It has gone on too long.

Ivan Watterland owns the only sizeable ranch between Prince George and McBride and he claims that in most areas you can't even grow good hay. In his opinion, the best use for most of this land is growing timber, yet the people who logged the preempted land can walk away without sowing a seed of grass or grain, and without planting one seedling. Few people outside this area know this is going on.

"Some people are even practising this type of procedure on good recreational land in the McLeod Lake area. The owners of cabins out there don't want the trees cut down. When the timber's gone, these so-called loggers usually pack up and leave, laughing all the way to the bank. If this procedure isn't stopped, it's going to be a sad day for B.C.. The government of this province must be more responsible with its land use.

"When we were growing up and working with our Dad in his old sawmill, Joe, we logged with horses. We only took out trees that suited our timber orders. When we were finished, the logged area looked just like a park. There were enough young trees left standing to drop their seeds and start a second forest. This was the sensible way, the right way, but look how it's all changed."

"Don't you think it's about time the management of our forests was taken away from the politicians?" I asked Bob. "There could be a permanent board set up that wouldn't be changed every time a new government was elected."

"Yes, I do, Joe. It's got to happen."

Bob Harkins believes that the people of British Columbia don't realize the enormous amount of wood that comes out of the northern Interior. Today the area is the largest softwood lumber-producing region in Canada. It produces 35 percent of B.C.'s total lumber output and some 20 percent of Canada's total production; a claim that translates into an annual lumber volume of five billion board feet. That's enough lumber to build 650,000 homes a year, or three times Canada's normal housing starts. One wonders whether the pioneer sawmill owners who had the foresight to establish the Northern Interior Lumbermen's Association half a century ago had any idea what they were starting.

But, as always, the emphasis is on the coastal forest industry with its rainforests and huge trees. So the northern Interior, as important as it is, still takes a back seat in the public theatre.

CHAPTER EIGHT

Northern Reporter

Ken Bernsohn is the Northern Editor for the Vancouver-based *Hiballer Forest Magazine*, and Prince George is his northern headquarters.

Ken is also an excellent reporter for the *Prince George Citizen* and has written *Cutting up the North*, a book he can well be proud of. Ken's specialties are the logging, lumbering and pulp industries. His "beat" requires travelling the back roads and most of the logging roads in the northern half of British Columbia, probably one of the largest assignments in Canada.

On November 5, 1990 I met Ken in the coffee shop of the Inn of the North for a taped interview. He showed me an article, hot off the press, from the *Citizen*, covering the weekend meeting of the newly-appointed British Columbia Forest Resources Commission, chaired by Sandy Peel. Some excerpts follow:

Our Forests: How do we divide the pie?

More than 30 representatives from forest companies, the Nechako Environmental Coalition, loggers, trappers, Native councils, the B.C. Steelhead Society and local government officials met for 12-1/2 hours at the Yellowhead Inn, reaching agreement on some issues, disagreeing on others.

General issues include the idea that the pie should be bigger (that there should be more forest resources through intensive management). Commission chairman Sandy Peel summed up the meeting, "that more attention should be paid to all resources (rather than just timber values) and that there should be secure funding for forest management in the broad sense. Increasing the size of the pie doesn't conflict with setting aside some additional forest areas for parks and to assure biological diversity," Peel said.

At this workshop, as at others across the province, people agreed there's a need for a new inventory of all resources, that the province needs a land use strategy rather than just making piecemeal decisions, and that there should be more local control of the forest, rather than decisions made in Victoria for the whole province, which may be right for some areas, but wrong for others.

To encourage exchange of ideas, the meeting was broken down into three work groups.

The discussion of land use strategy demonstrated the different values people brought to the meeting.

Flemming Einfeldt, representing the Association of B.C. Professional Foresters, told one group any land use strategy should deal with the whole land base of the province, not just the provincial forests.

Mary Coulter of the Nechako Environmental Coalition was concerned that mining and other activities which affect the environment should be included.

Rancher and logging contractor Howard Lloyd wanted to be sure the rules were "the same for the big companies and for the small guys."

Dave Lehane of the Mackenzie Chamber of Commerce said, "We need an evolving strategy, not one etched in stone," and Russell Alec of the Necoslie Indian band asked how a strategy could be put in place before native land claims were settled.

"We need goals, and goal posts," Lehane said.

"At the moment, we have no rules; the loudest group gets its way."

The discussion continued for an hour with everyone at the meeting having their say, and gradually tending to agree with Jim Burbee of Northwood Pulp and Timber that there should be both top-down and bottom-up decision-making, with the province setting a framework, but with decisions about how to reach these goals made regionally and locally, dealing with small areas only and with as many people involved in each decision as possible.

As we sipped coffee, Ken explained the situation in northern B.C.: "Northwest of Prince George, great volumes of timber were open to submissions for acquisition from the adjacent towns, and some not so adjacent, in the expectation that the rail line (formerly the Pacific Great Eastern, but re-named B.C. Rail) would be maintained so the various companies could haul their logs to market. The entire route was actually approved after W.A.C. Bennett (the province's premier from 1952 to 1972) had flown the route by helicopter back in the '60s. Parts of this rail line had actually been laid on plywood where it crossed the muskeg.

"At the same time, there was an immense beetle infestation about 130 miles southeast of Prince George in the Bowron Valley. All the lumber companies operating in the Prince George Timber Supply Area were told to move their equipment into the Bowron to utilize the timber and control the beetles."

As a result, they created a clearcut that can be seen from the moon with the naked eye. According to Ken Bernsohn, it's the largest clearcut in the world, but it was a job that had to be done because these vast spruce forests were dying.

When the companies had finished with this spruce budworm beetle-infested timber, they had to move out of the area because of the overcut. Hardly a tree was left standing. They were alloted timber and told to move their logging operations back up to the Sustut and Takla areas by the winter of 1990.

With the ill-advised B.C. Rail line in the Sustut having been abandoned in 1980, there was the obvious problem of getting the timber to market. Private industry moved in and formed two consortiums to repair it, one from the Houston-Smithers area to the east and the other from Prince George. Then the companies naturally began arguing about who would pay for what. It was estimated that it would cost a whopping $32 million to make the rail line operational. They squabbled for over a year. Then B.C. Rail stepped in and said, in effect, "Thank you for your studies. We now know we can do it cheaper and intend to start right away."

B.C. Rail said it would collect the cost by charging freight. The log and lumber people were understandably upset. The timber was 70 miles closer to Vanderhoof, but was being hauled right past that village into Prince George for an overall distance of 400 miles. The timber would also be going right through Fort St. James north of Vanderhoof. So the government held public hearings. Consequently, at the hearings, all the towns within that 400 mile distance declared they needed and had a right to that timber.

The Cabinet, in a move attacked by the ombudsman (the government-appointed but independently-minded arbitrator of public issues), overruled his decision and determined that the wood should indeed go as previously promised to processing plants in Prince George.

"It's a very simple thing. Somebody has to suffer. The question is who?" said Ken.

The decision was made after the railroad had been rebuilt up through the Driftwood Valley. Rustad Bros. and Northwood, two big operators, were already preparing to haul part way by rail and then by highway trucks from the area, starting the end of November, 1990.

"I was pretty upset about the whole thing," Ken said. "I felt it should go to the closer towns to improve and help their economy. Some of these towns are suffering. On the other hand, if a pulp mill can utilize trees down to two inches, and have that standard of manufacturing here in Prince George, then they deserve some of that wood.

"It depends on the mill. Lakeland in Prince George is doing a tremendous job. You really should have a good look at that mill. They have installed the first electronically-controlled end-dogging system. It just picks up a log by the ends, then scans and selects a thousand ways to get the most value out of that log before making the first cut. This scanning process is done six times a minute. It really boggles the mind. This makes it possible to process 5,760 logs during a normal two eight-hour shift day." Even though there are only 16 people on the floor of the mill, they produce 130 million board feet of lumber a year. By rebuilding the mill they began getting up to 30 percent more lumber from the average log. Then they put in a new planer mill and began getting 12 percent more lumber on top of that. "This mill is run by three local guys, George Killy, Ivan Anderson and Bob Stewart. George's father used to own Ferguson Lake Sawmill back in the '50s. Ivan Anderson and Bob Stewart worked at Sinclair Spruce Lumber up until 1956. Then they moved to Prince George and got into the sawmill business here. George was looking around for a burner as a way to heat the mill and at the same time utilize the waste. And as you very well know, Joe, there used to be one hell of a lot of waste. In fact, the waste of good wood was mind-boggling. But when they got into this new style of production there was little or no waste to burn. Everybody wins, nobody loses.

"These guys won Canada's Award for Excellence for cooperation and technological change the first year it was awarded. This was shared with the IWA. The workers were involved from the day the decision was made to put in the new planer. They installed the equipment themselves, working along with the manufacturer's representatives. Because of the workers' attitude, the mill was up and running in one third the scheduled time. If there ever was an example of worker-management cooperation, this was it.

Ken had recently visited the Lakeland mill to see some equipment brought in from Germany to do specialty product manufacturing. The first day this equipment was operating, the workers on the plant floor shut it down. When the manager asked, "What's the problem?" He got a quick reply.

"Well, the equipment seems fine, but the conveyors leading up to it and taking the lumber away are not fast enough. We're going to make some changes," the floor boss said. Within an hour everything was working perfectly.

"In the late '70s and early '80s, we were hearing statements coming out of Victoria, like: 'What do we owe these towns in the north?' or 'What do we owe Burns Lake?' or 'Who cares if Hazelton dies?' There was also the argument of labour mobility versus community stability. The fact is, that to this day it's never been resolved to the satisfaction of these northern communities," Ken said.

I asked, "Have they ever thought of growing trees out there? They would have their jobs and keep the people and their towns if they'll do that."

"Not necessarily. It also requires some smarts on the part of the sawmills," Ken replied. "Decorate Forest Products in Burns Lake is very innovative. They've produced over 50 specialty products and are shipping processed logs to Japan for home building. They're also growing trees everywhere they've harvested. They should certainly receive a substantial piece of that forestry pie but, because Burns Lake has less voting power than Prince George, the government ruled in favour of Prince George."

This mill has also initiated some interesting marketing technology. Ken recalls a conversation he had with George Killy:

"You see packaged lumber riding along on rail cars, and on the wrapping it says 'Decorate Forest Products' or 'MacMillan Bloedel'. Who cares about that? If you're shipping to Koffman & Broad, one of the largest home builders in California, why not put 'Part of another fine Koffman & Broad Home' on it? Why not customize your lumber crafts for the bigger customers? It won't make you more money, but it could keep you in with your customers when times get tough."

George thought about it, and phoned Marsh Brothers, a manufacturing firm in the Lower Mainland. It took them four years to put it all together. They now have a computerized system that can take any individual parcel of lumber and put what they want on the wrapping. They just enter it into a computer and tell it how big and what colour they want the letters. They're now customizing their lumber wraps for over 100 customers and it's paying off."

"I'm keenly interested in what the industry is doing up in this north country to grow trees, Ken."

"Growing trees ain't the trick," Ken replied. "This year we have somewhere in the neighbourhood of 66 million trees being planted in this region. It's more trees than were planted in all of British Columbia up through 1965. For years, all we planted in this province was a mixture of spruce, pine and fir. Unfortunately, that doesn't put the right trees in the right places. That takes experience. Several companies in this area are now doing a lot of experimenting with Siberian Larch. Not one person in a thousand knows this, but it's important.

"It's only been since the late '80s that companies have been growing their own seedlings for planting. Up to that time they had to buy their trees directly from government nurseries which weren't producing enough to satisfactorily restock their logged-over areas. It's a very messy story. Ross Reid says if you want to blame someone, there's blame enough for everyone."

I asked, "Do you think the registered professional forester of today knows enough about what he's doing?" I said it with a smile, and he laughed.

"No. He needs more experience out in the woods. The values people now want from their forests are more than just lumber. When you clearcut you aid certain forms of wildlife. You hurt others. Nature is like that. We just had two fascinating experiments this summer.

"Prince George Wood Preservers went in and selectively logged, leaving trees with lichen for the caribou to nibble on. They did it in a very complex pattern. They removed only about 20 percent of the trees in that forest, but over 40 percent of the fibre. The caribou herds are now increasing and doing very well. These herds have been very carefully monitored. Previously, and remember this, if there were caribou in an area, there'd be no logging allowed. This thinning of the timber by selective logging with experienced people is working so well that Prince George Wood Preservers are being allowed extra quota.

"The second experiment involves the Workers' Compensation Board allowing the logging companies, for the first time ever, to leave standing snags. The snags provide homes for woodpeckers, which in turn help control the bark beetles and other insects that attack and kill the trees. They also provide other wildlife habitat for as long as they stand. In fact, we have six different species of woodpeckers up here that attack the beetle.

"The cabs of the new feller-bunchers are so sturdy, that if a tree breaks and falls on the machine the operator is completely safe in

Feller Buncher

A big backhoe, equipped with a tree clamp and heavy duty circular saw, which can travel over rough ground and low-cut stumps. It clamps on to a tree, cuts it off and swings it to the side, placing it in a pile or bunch ready to be skidded to the nearest truck landing for loading.

the cab. Compensation rules forbid the operator to get out of the cab while cutting or stacking trees.

"Can they successfully thin with these feller-bunchers?" I asked.

"No, because of the width of the equipment versus the width of the path through the trees."

"Well, perhaps you have to sacrifice that path," I said

"That's what we're doing. Under the Forest Resources Development Agreement, they discovered that a lot of areas where junk trees grew back, it worked. But there was one area near Dawson Creek where they thought they had good natural regeneration, and it turned out to be 1,200 hectares of junk brush, just trash, when they went in to inspect it. In other words, the stands that were logged up to 1972 are not satisfactorily restocked. Who is at fault? Take your pick. In some places the trees are too close together and don't have room to grow. It's a very complex problem in this area."

"That's why I'm talking feller-bunchers," I said, making my point again.

"In most areas, the roots of the lodgepole pine rarely go more than 13 inches under the soil, so when you remove too many trees from an area, the others are liable to blow down. Just lack of protection."

"That's the trouble with leaving seed trees, Ken. Sixty percent of them are blown down within a year. I was south of Quesnel yesterday, and looked at an area where my brother and I had logged 40 years ago and there were only a very few of the old seed trees standing. But there's one hell of a good stand of young timber there that needs to be commercially thinned.

"How long do you figure it would take to grow a crop of merchantable trees in the Prince George working circles if it was intensively managed?" I asked Ken.

"There are as many different opinions out there as there are people. I realize that's no answer, but this industry is full of unanswered questions."

Garner Road 20 miles south of Quesnel, November, 1990

Naturally restocked fir and pine. Fir seed trees were left when logging was done by the author in 1953. This stand is obviously ready for selective thinning.

"Well, it would depend on the intensity of the tree farming," I suggested.

"No, no, that isn't the main problem here. We only have an average of 75 frost-free days during a normal year. And that's what you'd call a short growing season. Under natural conditions, trees reach the peak of their growth in about 70 years and then they slow down. But there's no rule that says we have to wait for a tree to reach that stage of growth before it can be harvested. In the southern U.S. they're growing trees for only 28 years because all they want is pulp. They use a special species of pine they call magazine trees. If you want to grow only for pulp you can do it here in about 35 years under natural conditions, with no fertilization," Ken said.

"The natural pine from this area is one of the toughest in the world according to a Swedish testing lab. Some mills here are using it to make furniture while others are making lodgepole pine flooring. It's very durable. Just like hardwood. All you do is put on a gymnasium floor finish, the same stuff they use in high schools. I have it in my house and, you know, in two years it hasn't needed even one waxing.

"The decision as to the best type of timber to grow should be based on the growing site. The higher, dryer and poorer sites produce slower growth and tougher timber. Medium sites produce trees suitable for lumber and pulp. The best sites produce fast-growing trees suitable for construction material, such as joists and 2x4s. There's where the money is. If you want 2x4s, with fertilization and thinning, you can get trees reaching their peak of growth in about 60 years. Up here in the north some experiments with lodgepole pine that started in the 1920s are still going on. But these stands have already passed their prime and should be cut.

"Steele, a Registered Professional Forester with Lakeland Mills, one of my favourite foresters in Canada, told me the company took some privately-owned land and began trying different ways of preparing the site to grow trees. They used harrows and disc trenchers with mounders, just like a farmer, and tried burning

117

and not burning, plus various chemical fertilizers. When I asked him what they'd learned from this his answer was, 'There are more ways to kill a seedling than anyone would ever imagine.'

"Ray Williston said something to me I thought very wise: 'It's very easy to criticize using hindsight, but when you're faced with a problem, just make the best guess you can.' I believe Ray made some good guesses, yet some of the things he did up here didn't work out worth a damn. But who is perfect?

"The pulp mills for the Interior were a mixed blessing. They've been an economic boom, plenty of jobs, but they've also meant dioxin in the rivers."

"Well, I suppose it's worthwhile if you're trying to utilize all the fibre," I said. "I must confess, when I was a logging contractor, fibre meant wood. Sometimes I still get confused. I wonder if the public out there realize that when we're talking fibre, we mean good old-fashioned wood?"

"Why does the timber have to be utilized? It's doing just fine out there in the bush," Ken snapped.

"Well it's strange that so few people think your way," I argued. "Most believe it's better to harvest and restock with another useful crop. So far we have not planted enough trees to guarantee future jobs in this province, a province where about 50 percent of our revenue comes from trees. We know that there is approximately 35 percent more capacity in the sawmills of B.C. than there are trees available to keep them going."

"Well, the most profitable forestry firm in Prince George right now has a total harvest of 100,000 cubic metres per year, which compared to the bigger companies is nothing. They are making tables, bookcases and furniture that is being sold by Ikea, the successful Swedish company. They make the best possible product and can sell into some very selective markets. They have found stable markets and they keep them by giving quality with service. Because of this, they don't have to worry about rising and falling demands in ordinary lumber markets. They don't even care that there's 22 percent more pulp production in B.C. than there was five years ago. As a result, when other sawmills are

118

losing money because of lumber prices, they are doing just fine. It's encouraging." On that note we said goodbye.

Then I drove to Prince Rupert to catch the ferry south to Port Hardy near the north end of Vancouver Island. This is always a beautiful trip. It amazes me to see mile after mile of old growth timber on both sides of the Inside Passage. There must be uncountable millions of cubic meters of good fir and hemlock already passed its prime and starting to develop dead tops. A lightning strike during the dry season could burn off whole mountain sides in a matter of hours.

Though the mountains go up very steeply from the ocean, I'm positive our loggers will some day be capable of harvesting all this timber either by helicopter, balloon or aerial cable. Down through the years, our gyppo loggers have been able to do the impossible and make it look easy. Without a doubt these dying trees will have to be replaced with vibrant young trees in the near future.

A year after our interview with Ken Bernsohn, the Forest Resources Commission has made some strong and necessary recommendations to the government of this province. It recommends immediate legislation for a single all-encompassing code of practices to be established through the introduction of a Forest Practices Act. This new act will outline the acceptable minimum standards for logging to sustain all resources—even ones we haven't discovered yet.

A Forest Practices Act will outline how and when land should be logged. It will set out the size, locations and timing of all future clearcuts. Even more importantly, it will set rules for protecting all of our resources, including water, wildlife, recreation areas and land to support silviculture.

Craig Piprell summarizes the situation in *Monday Magazine's* August 22, 1991, edition:

> Who would have guessed, for example, that the bark of the slow growing Pacific yew tree was going to provide a rare and valuable treatment for breast and ovarian cancer? Our forest experts thought the Pacific yew was a weed.

119

Pictures courtesy of *Monday Magazine*, June 1990, showing MacMillan Bloedel clearcuts reaching to the edge of once remote Nahmint Lake.

Right: Groves in the Nahmint watershed contain up to three times more timber per hectare than the Carmanah Valley.

Nahmint River Watershed

With draft legislation for a forest practices act already in circulation—like the Tin-Wis Coalition's Forest Stewardship Act and the Village of Hazelton's Forest Industry Charter of Rights—the forest industry has suddenly gotten interested in devising "voluntary guidelines." Too little, too late. Decades of guidelines and industry self-regulation have led to "progressive" clearcuts, charred slash, and rivers that run like chocolate pudding when it rains. It doesn't take a rocket scientist to figure out why. "They" say the bad stuff all happened in the past. But it's happening right now. And the only way to stop it is to make bad forest practices a criminal offence....

Instead, in future—as the Forest Resources Commission and other groups point out—when we allow government and industry to manage public forests the key words must be "responsibility" and "accountability." When a transnational logging company like Fletcher Challenge destroys public resources in the name of a quick buck—with the Forests Ministry's blessing—the regular folks who own the resource must be able to identify the responsible culprits wherever and whoever they are, and hold them legally accountable.

The B.C. Forest Resources Commission has recommended that public participation in the planning management of forest land-based activities be legislated. So far, however, public input continues to accomplish very little. What is needed here is a more educated general public. Politicians still decide how, when and if public input is to be considered. Presently there is no legal requirement that public input be involved in forest management. Craig Piprell in Victoria's *Monday Magazine* wrote it this way:

> In fact, politicians should be distanced from future routine forest management decisions as much as possible, advises the Forest Resources Commission. Given current discretionary powers, the Premier, Cabinet and Forests Minister all exercise immense political clout in B.C.'s public forests. For example, ex-Socred Forests Minister Dave Parker—an ex-corporate logger, now Minister of Parks and Lands—inappropriately (and politically) interfered

with the award of a forest licence in Takla-Sustut in north-central B.C. In his annual report to the legislature last spring, the provincial Ombudsman reported "inappropriate interference by a Cabinet minister" in the granting of the licences. Shades of "Honest Bob" Sommers and the awarding of the licence to B.C. Forest Products some 35 years ago. The Ombudsman suggested the Forests Ministry reconsider its decision. The Forests Ministry decided not to.

Then last month the village of Hazelton took the whole matter to the B.C. Supreme Court for a judicial hearing. Hazelton wants the Forest Ministry's decision overturned, the forest licence application reopened—and damages for the loss of the licence.

It is significant that villages like Hazelton are challenging government decisions and insisting that there be more public input into forest management. It's time to cut out the dead wood of government and the meddling of politicians so our forest industry can become healthy again. We should heed the B.C. Forest Resources Commission's recommendation to legislate public participation in the planning of forest land-based activities.

CHAPTER NINE

A Native's Submission for Change

Matt Vickers, a Registered Professional Forester with his own consulting company in New Hazelton, spoke to the Truck Loggers' Convention on the topic of *Tenure*. I found it gratifying to find that the young native's ideas on this critical topic coincided in so many instances with my own. I, therefore, intend to pass them on. He framed his presentation on tenure in the context of 'Managing Change.' He sees three critical issues regarding that change with respect to the way we manage our forests.

Vicker's report lists three considerations:

First, the conflict between the environmental movement and the industry is only the symptom of a deeper problem.

Second, with the passing of the 1980s we have seen our world fundamentally altered by technology. It behooves us to change or create new institutions for the 21st Century, which will not only serve our current needs, but more importantly will serve future generations. Nowhere is this more critical than in the job of managing our forests which take generations to grow.

Third, with British Columbia's population projected to increase from 3 million to 8 million early in the next century, we must address today the issues of the future. As a major engine in the economy of British Columbia, our forest resources will serve to attract new people, new ideas and new capital for tourism, recreation and a host of other resources, but they must also continue to supply us with the natural essentials to our quality of living.

Vickers presented a synopsis of what he believed will be necessary in terms of tenure to meet today's and tomorrow's challenges:

Included in market values are forest products, energy, tourism, recreation, fisheries, trapping, grazing, medicinal products and mineral access.

Ecological values include water, soil and wildlife habitat. Because these resources are renewable, they can be managed to fulfill the needs of future generations. The practical question is, "How can we do all this?"

The Forest Resources Commission, in their options paper, reported that the 1,700 plus written submissions could be assembled into three main groups.

The first vision called for continuation of the 'status quo.'

The second vision was for the complete preservation of forest lands.

But the third vision was what I found illuminating. It called for a major change in the use and management of forest lands, enhanced stewardship of all forest resources, and growth targets which would be achieved through intensive, integrated forest resource management, including intensive silviculture.

It is my view that only a progressive alternative such as that stated in the third vision can overcome the confrontations between major tenure holders and conservation groups.

Admittedly it is difficult to focus on these future issues. As matters stand now, future projections for the forest show declining forest products in terms of annual cut. This shrinkage is coupled with an excessive concentration in one product segment, pulp and paper. Continuation of this trend in conjunction with the projected decreases in timber supply will lead us down a path of reduced employment and economic disaster.

We have some of the world's preeminent conditions for growing softwoods—the climate, tree species, topography and soil make British Columbia an unparalleled place to grow high quality forests. Based on his experience as a professional forester, Vickers believes the potential exists in our forests to increase growth and yield as much as 100 percent. Eighty percent of the growth increase can come from doing proper reforestation. The remaining 20 percent will come from intensive forest management practices such as commercial thinning, fertilization, tree improvement and site preparation.

The greatest impediment is brought about by the requirement in the *Forest Act* that ties TFLs and Forest Licences to manufacturing facilities. The high degree of annual allowable cut apportioned to FLs and TFLs and the lack of a competitive log market is a hazard to the industry's future.

As a direct consequence of not having a competitive log market we have low log prices, lower profits from woodland operations and less money to re-invest in the forest.

Sources of increased utilization would include:

a) Greater use of low grade logs in the pulping process;
b) Tightening of current utilization standards (decreasing stump heights and top sizes);
c) Increased utilization of commercial and juvenile thinnings as a roundwood supply for pulpmills; and
d) More extensive logging of less accessible sites and economically marginal stands during strong market periods or as technology changes.

Vickers, as a free enterprise entrepreneur, believes that the open free marketplace is the best mechanism for allocating resources to their highest value and best end-use.

Vickers goes on to suggest that any new tenure system should contain the following elements:

a) There must be a greater security of tenure best facilitated by extending the term of licences to encourage investment in the resource;
b) The forest land base should be privatized to create an environment for stewardship and enhanced growth;
c) Converting plants and mills should have only a portion of their wood supply requirements provided through long-term tenure. The balance should be through a province-wide competitive log market. This is necessary in order that our manufacturing sector can maintain its competitive ability, attract capital investment, foster increased efficiency and provide for community stability; and

d) As a requirement, tenure must provide for the protection and management of other resources. True integrated management must be practised to allow sustainable development to become a reality.

Vickers suggests we need to create and adopt diversity in our tenure structure. To facilitate this he recommends three tenure forms:

a) Area-based Tree Farm Licences;
b) Area-based Forest Management Tenures; and
c) Woodlot Licences.

Area-based Tree Farm Licences

Instead of a significant proportion of the annual allowable cut being held for independent mill operators and enterprise loggers participating in a vigorous competitive market, the tenure system in B.C. has become closed and rigid. What is now required is more diverse types of tenure holdings.

This type of diversity is evident in other forest jurisdictions around the world. An analysis of self-sufficiency ratios of owned and controlled timber on the part of public corporations in other forest industry jurisdictions illustrates tenure diversity. For example, in the U.S. as a whole, manufacturers hold an average of approximately 40 percent of their fibre supply needs in secured tenure of some form, usually fee-simple ownership. In Sweden, the proportion is even lower. One-quarter of the annual harvest is generated from company-owned forest lands, with another 25 percent from public lands, and 50 percent from an array of private land-holders.

From this evidence, I have come to the view that a certain ratio of the annual fibre supply needs of operating plants and mills in the industry should emanate from a secure timber tenure base. In British Columbia these tenures are the Forest Licences and Tree Farm Licences. Furthermore, these tenures need to be strengthened beyond the existing terms, both in duration and in protection against withdrawals.

126

If a mill were closed, or bought for its timber rights and then shut down, the tenures would lapse with the mill or plant in question. In essence, maintenance of production and jobs would be a condition of the tenure.

In practice, Vickers suggests that present TFLs and Forest Licences be re-apportioned at about 50 percent of their present size in annual volume terms into area-based Tree Farm Licences. These new Tree Farm Licences would all be area-based, thus TFLs and Forest Licences in Timber Sale Areas would be "rolled over" at a ratio of half their present annual volume. While these tenures would be intended to be more secure than is the case presently (although still short of a privatization component), they could not be transferred without consent, and this consent would need to include the strong consideration of the viewpoint of the affected community.

Each of the new TFLs should be reviewed on a case-by-case basis in order to determine the level of contract and company operations to be required for that licence. In this manner, dislocation can be minimized in forest-based communities while at the same time the introduction of a major program of forest renewal would provide greater opportunities for the future.

Area-based Forest Management Tenures

As a new form of licence, these tenures would be much smaller in average size than the large-scale corporate licences which now exist. The rationale for smaller tenures is simple— intensive management of the forest land base and the tasks and targets of increased growth and yield are best applied on the smaller tenures.

Indeed, examples of small tenures found in other jurisdictions like Sweden have a historical pattern for success in instituting advanced silviculture and forest management programs through the full range of intermediate tasks such as brushing, spacing and thinning, to the final 'stump to dump' phases of harvesting and marketing. This approach to tenure would permit a movement towards a state of integrated resource management beyond any achievable under current tenure arrangements.

This level of intensive and integrated resource management can be achieved via two mechanisms, either by regulation or by management regimes incorporated in the overall resource development. There are three possible sources of funding to meet these costs:

a) User fees for those values which can be economically measured and have a market able to reasonably determine pricing and allocation; for example recreation areas;

b) Costs borne by the tenure holder and paid out of the sale of logs for activities which can be justified as being legitimate operating costs (i.e. protection of fish habitat); and

c) Funding from existing government programs for management activities which are deemed beneficial to society but which have no marketplace or are above legitimate operating costs. For example, creation of ungulate habitat through prescribed burning.

These new tenures are intended to be awarded by competitive process. However, I recommend that three criteria be reviewed in the awarding of every proposal. The first criterion should be the level and degree of management activities proposed. The second criterion should be a monetary bid. Third and most important, there should be local demonstrated knowledge, experience and performance (and its implicit relationship to community stability). Because the primary goal is to realize the growth potential of our forests, the bid proposal process would emphasize professional qualifications, local experience and area knowledge, plus financial stability.

Potential tenure holders should include communities, municipalities, local Indian bands, forestry corporations, forest consultants, logging contractors and silvicultural companies. The flexibility of size offered by these tenures will provide for a diversity of forest managers.

In order to maintain the fairness and integrity of this program and to ensure protection against any possible abuse, the awarding of new tenures should be determined on an independent basis. For these purposes, I would recommend the following measures:

  a) The competitive bidding and awards procedure should be an open public process with clear guidelines and criteria. This process should also include an appeal mechanism;

  b) The awards should be determined by an independent allocation board preferably one to each region or major forest zone with recommendations forwarded to the Chief Forester of the province; and

  c) Given the new importance of this role, the position and office of the Chief Forester should report directly to the legislature in the same manner as the Auditor-General and Ombudsman, to ensure and protect his or her impartiality.

Woodlot Licences

Earlier I mentioned privatization as a vehicle towards enhanced stewardship. I felt that the privatization of the woodlot program has great potential to involve everyday British Columbians in forest management and to also create a cultural connection between themselves and the forest. The potential is also there to get good intensive management from the woodlots.

Twenty percent of the total forest tenures should be in the form of woodlot licences, with the intention that these would subsequently be privatized on 10-year option or first refusal basis, provided full performance to intensive forestry standards has been met. From these tenures logs would be sold in a competitive open market.

The new woodlot tenures would be more flexible than the current program, allowing for a diversity of sizes and a range of opportunities for Canadians to manage the forest. This type of program would enhance tenure diversity.

I believe the types of tenure proposed above are the kind that can solve our immediate problems and meet our long-term needs.

CHAPTER TEN

Carving out a Logging Curriculum

Awareness, belief and commitment have launched many community-based programs and locally-developed school courses. The Clearwater Secondary School Logging Curriculum is the story of the development of one such course.

Clearwater, in central British Columbia, is a scattered community of about 4,000 near the junction of the North Thompson and Clearwater rivers. The town started as a Canadian National railway station. Now, it is on the busy Highway 5, handling through-traffic from Kamloops on to Jasper and Edmonton. It is also the turn-off to Wells Gray Provincial Park, so Clearwater provides services for the tourist trade. But its main industry is lumber production.

Dr. Jim London, who now works for the University of Victoria, was principal of the Clearwater Secondary School in the early 1980s and saw the need for a logging program in the school system. At that time, he met with Bill Jory, the District Superintendent of Schools, and Jean Nelson, a dedicated local school trustee, to discuss the possibility of setting up a locally-based forestry course in the district's only secondary school. They agreed that the program should be non-academic and designed to satisfy the needs of those students who would be leaving school, either before or after graduation, to work directly in the logging industry.

Under Jim's guidance, the organizing committee decided the teaching emphasis should be on safety in practical logging skills. While academically oriented students would not be discouraged from taking the logging course, the aim would be to satisfy the needs of students who would be seeking immediate employment in the woods.

Jim remembers hearing remarks like: "Goddammit, Jim, you can't do this. The IWA will be upset. Kids cutting trees will be infringing on the loggers' jobs. The Workers' Compensation Board won't allow it. They'll say it's too dangerous. You've got to go through the big companies to get permission to cut trees. You'll never even be able to get started."

London heard many negatives. Yet, once the committee was formed, industry and the community became very supportive. He can't recall one refusal for assistance from an individual or organization.

Jim modified a curriculum used by the instructor of an alternate education class in Lumby, east of Vernon. The IWA, the two big mills, the B.C. Forest Service and the Workers' Compensation Board all said, in effect: "Wonderful. Great. What can we do to help?"

The committee faced three major problems: (a) acquiring a block of timber to cut, (b) providing the necessary equipment for their neophyte loggers, and (c) locating a qualified teacher.

Each turned out to be no problem. Officials in the B.C. Forest Service were enthusiastic about the concept of training young loggers. Without hesitation, they allocated a block of forest land close to the town and provided the necessary cutting permits at reasonable stumpage rates.

From the beginning, London believed the logging program could become self-supporting if it were properly managed and had community support. The North Thompson School District released $4,000 for the purchase of power saws, small tools and safety equipment. Trustee Nelson's late husband provided, on "permanent loan," a 440 John Deere track skidder.

There were no course specifics on logging available from the B.C. Ministry of Education, but none were needed by the veteran industrial educator who volunteered to develop a curriculum and teach the fundamentals of safe logging.

131

Bob Slingsby had been teaching at Clearwater Senior Secondary School for two decades. During his early years in the community he had spent his summers working in the woods. He was an experienced faller and logger who knew the industry from stump to the manufacturing plants and, just as importantly, he knew the people he could call on for help to make the program work.

London's dream of a logging program was off to a good start. He reported on the success of the program in a brief he submitted to the Royal Commission on Education some seven years later. He was able to report that 10 percent of their school population each year had at least five months of training in safety and logging procedures. His report recommended that the provincial government should assist in the development of similar programs throughout the province. He proposed suggestions which could lead to post-secondary enhancement in subject areas related directly to the province's major industry. Jim stated in his written report:

> Most of the 'Funds for Excellence' have been expended on computer hardware and training programs related to its use. Indeed, we in School District #26, like students and educators elsewhere, have benefitted from government expenditures in this area. We appreciate the government's assistance in expanding our computer program.
>
> What concerns us, however, is the narrowness of focus of our present government. Very few of the students currently registered in British Columbia schools today will make a living in the computer industry. But many of our students will be employed in the forest industry, the backbone of our provincial economy.
>
> There are in our province more than 30 logging communities like Clearwater. They continue to be a major source of our province's wealth. What the Clearwater Woodlot Educational Society would like to have the Commission recommend to the provincial government is a return to local autonomy for school boards. Local boards are well aware of their community's greatest needs and, in our opinion, should be given more discretion in choosing how educational funds are to be spent. We believe that such a change

would encourage small school districts to initiate successful programs like the Clearwater Secondary School Logging Program and, in so doing, serve their students better.

In the fall of 1990, nine years after their program was initiated, I interviewed Bob Slingsby in his office at the Clearwater Secondary School, and asked him how the logging program was progressing and what he thought of it after nine years.

Bob proudly replied, "Since last June, we've kept up our numbers in the forestry class. At present our class has 24 students. Last year we had 26 studying and working at logging.

"The total project is now funded entirely through the sale of the logs we produce. We're still trying to get some extra money from the government to buy newer equipment. That's our biggest cost. We've recently put a down payment on a second Cat out of our earned funds. This machine has been used less than 1,000 hours and it will cost us only $50,000. That's less than half its appraised value."

"You certainly should be eligible for a grant to make such purchases," I suggested.

"That's what we've been trying to get. We made a compelling submission to the Royal Commission on Education in Kamloops last year. Dr. Jim London wrote it for us. He also lobbied our local MLAs, Bud Smith and Claude Richmond, but so far no extra funds are in sight. We are barely managing to keep our heads above water since we bought this equipment. We pay for all repairs, lubricants and fuel with no government funding, even though it's an integral and necessary part of the students' training. Without fuel, lube oil, grease and reasonably up-to-date machinery, it's impossible to teach any young would-be machine operator how to log and build roads."

"If the Forests or Education ministries could arrange to let you pay only a token stumpage price for your timber of, say, one dollar per cubic metre, that's all you'd ever need," I suggested.

"That's one thing they've refused to consider," Slingsby declared. "They just will not change the stumpage rates. The criteria for setting stumpage in the first place is by taking production costs from the average efficient logger. We pay the same price for our timber the big mills pay.

"When starting in September with green kids, we'll be lucky to put down more than 10 trees a day, and that's the way I want it. I don't want them to get involved in highball production at the beginning. Teach them the rules of safety first, then work up to a normal production rate.

"One of the main reasons we started this program was because a high percentage of our grade nine and ten students were dropping out and going to work in the woods. They'd show up with a power saw, bucking pads and a hard hat. You'd see some of these same boys cut up and on workers' compensation a week later. That's when we realized they should at least be taught basic falling skills and safe handling of chain saws. The best way to teach young people to log safely is to let them be there and do the work under proper supervision. This way they can be forewarned of the dangers and taught how to deal with them.

"We try to start students on this logging course in Grade 10 when most are 15 to 16 years old. Initially, the biggest problem is making them realize it's not just a way of getting out of the classroom. We take them out logging for one full day every two weeks. Last year I had five groups, so that meant one week I had two groups out and the next week three. Of course, they miss some classes, so that creates another problem. The other teachers say they should be at their regular classes all the time. However, I still feel that we are keeping a lot of students in school who would have dropped out if this program had not been available to them."

"Do most of your students have a job waiting for them when they finish your logging course?" I asked.

"Yes, the better ones do. Some of them drop out along the way when they realize that logging is not for them. Some of them are frightened by it and find it's better to keep working at the books. They can learn a lot about themselves in a hurry by working in the woods. Most of our last year's students are already employed in the industry. Several of the students I have now in Grade 12

134

worked all through their summer holidays on road-building machines or driving skidders.

"They'll fall and buck one day, then get on a machine the next time out. At that age they seem to handle the machines well in a reasonably short period of time.

"Later in the year, when we find some students don't want to do falling—they just can't seem to get the cuts right all the time—we encourage them to try other specialties, such as scaling or servicing the equipment.

"Last year all our bulletin boards in the classroom were full of posters showing serious accidents. I keep reminding the class that there are people with 30 and 40 years experience who are no longer with us because they made just one bad mistake. Before we start a day in the woods I remind them that it's a hazardous business unless they take the time to work safely.

"Those power saws can be as dangerous as a loaded gun. I like the students to use hand tools for the first while. They need to know why they're making undercuts, why they're making them a specific size, and what to look out for—widow-makers and dead tops, rot and slope—and always have an escape route planned. One of the things we had to develop was good practical safety information.

"The manual I have here was put together by a man named Steve Holland, who lives and works over on Vancouver Island. Steve did a phenomenal amount of work getting his facts and demonstrations together and I've used this as my basic safety textbook. It covers the theory of falling, undercuts, the correct amount of holding wood to be left, winds, and the decisions to be made about where the trees should fall. It goes on to explain other things connected with the making of a good log.

"Initially, Steve had it printed for farmers and weekend woodcutters. People who go out for firewood are usually falling the two most dangerous types of material: dead snags and heavy leaners. Steve was a power saw instructor and put his manual together with the help of the Workers' Compensation Board. I've added several things that are helpful to our students."

"I couldn't agree with you more, Bob," I told him. "Logging starts with falling. To drop those trees so they don't break, then buck for grade and scale is really one of the most important parts of a logging operation. I have said this to our own crews dozens of times over the years."

"Every year we get information about new fire-fighting equipment from the B.C. Forest Service. They help instruct our students in an approved fire suppression course. At the end of the course, the class is tested. If they pass the exam, they get a fire suppression card stamped by an official from the Forest Service. It's important; it gives the holder a rating in the industry as an experienced fire fighter.

"A former student who is now working at the coast was back here talking to me last spring. While he was working on a high-lead show at Port Hardy on Vancouver Island, he was given the opportunity to take helicopter training. He had just received his pilot's licence and had been offered a job to go heli-logging as co-pilot and was really excited about it. This young fellow was in one of our first classes and was the type of student that when a class-mate would say, 'I'm not sure I can get down into that ravine to drag those logs out,' he'd volunteer, 'Get off the machine, and I'll show you how to do it'. He would do this in a way that didn't offend or embarrass his schoolmate. He knew what he and the machine could do, and proceeded to do it. He had all the confidence in the world. He grew up in the bush and he'll probably always be there."

I asked Bob if there was any way we could help promote his logging course with this book; perhaps help get his program properly funded within the school system. Other schools in B.C. should be doing what's being done in Clearwater. It's both necessary and commendable.

"The B.C. Forest Service seems to worry about this little bit of timber they allow us to cut each year," Bob complained. "Why, I don't know. Forty truck loads is a drop in the bucket. It should be double that. Every three months we have to come up with $5,000 just for our Cat payments. This will go on for several more years

Students in the Clearwater Secondary School logging program. Back Row: Teacher Bob Slingsby standing between their two track skidders. Front Row: Students, left to right: David Wallace, Carter Oettli, Lance Richards, Steve Schulte, Kevin Lowe, Larry Gallot and Alan Vandenborre.

unless we can get a grant or are allowed more timber at reasonable prices. We couldn't get any government funding at all when we wanted to start our program here nine years ago.

"Joe Wadlegger, just down the hill about two kilometers, ran his D-6 up to our timber and put in all the roads and landings at no expense to us. Then we went out and felled trees and cut them into logs. That's all we could do for the first while. Then we had logs cut, but nothing to skid them with.

"As Jim London probably told you, Jean Nelson, our trustee from Blue River, and her husband Don, who was later killed in a logging accident, had this little 440 John Deere skidder. He called it 'his old gear jammer', but quickly added, 'It'll probably do the job for you'. He sent it down on a lowbed and it worked well.

"Then Dave Tremblay came along with his loader and, in just a couple of days, piled the logs for us. We kept on falling and yarding until we had our yearly quota finished. Then Tremblay came back with his loader and truck and hauled the logs to the mill, again at no charge. All this free help is what enabled us to produce enough timber to make the down payment on our second Cat.

"But I don't think we're any further ahead now. We have the two machines, but one isn't paid for. However, this second Cat is just like new. It has a six-way hydraulic blade. It's a good practical machine for students to learn on. There's no sense being out there with outdated equipment because it doesn't teach those future loggers anything about the up-to-date machines they will be expected to operate. The program also needed to buy a crew bus to transport the students to the work site and back to the school.

"This year we have two girls in our class. I've had girls before, but to date only one has stuck out the full three years. She was just an excellent faller, very meticulous. These two new girls want to run equipment. They just can't wait to get up there in the driver's seat of the skidder or that new Cat. Those girls operate as well, if not better, than some of our boys.

138

"But we can't turn out a full-fledged logger. That takes more time. During the last three years, our students have been getting out for only one full day every two weeks. If you start adding that up, it's not a great deal of time. However, they have learned to work safely and can handle power saws, skidders or Cats in a reasonably safe manner."

"Have you thought about teaching these young people how to plant and grow trees?" I asked Bob. "Maybe establish a small tree farm so they can plant, prune and properly learn that phase of forestry? If the province doesn't start something like that soon, there will be little or no timber left for your students to log."

"We haven't gone into that," he said, "although this is the direction we're trying to take now. We had a woodlot here, but with such a small quota we found we couldn't afford it. They expected us to do development work when we don't have sufficient money. Our machinery is not big enough for site preparation, so we'd have had to lease. We actually gave the woodlot back last year with their promise to supply us with the same quota of timber every year out in the same general area. It's close to the school, which is a plus for everyone. They want us to contract some thinning projects for them and get the students involved in planting. I'm almost sure we will be treating this as part of our full course as early as next year."

"Any nursery work, or signs of a nursery developing in this area?"

"No, not in Clearwater as yet. What I have right now is a complete program on managing a woodlot. We hope to teach this to our Grade 12 students in case they want to get involved in that kind of work when they graduate. There is a nursery down near Kamloops. We had some students who went on to the British Columbia Institute of Technology and became involved in intensive forestry.

"Maybe this is where you could almost demand funds," I suggested. "I believe they might be forthcoming quite readily if you taught tree planting. You'd probably need to have more students to make it worthwhile. The timber industry of British Columbia is still learning how to properly grow trees, and they'd better start teaching our young people pretty soon if they expect to have any lumber or pulp-related industries in the future. There must be appreciation for the trees. They are the things that keep the manufacturing plants in business and making a profit.

"I've been down to a couple of workshops at the nursery in Vernon where they are growing the seedlings and producing some very 'plus tree stock.' I haven't had a chance to take my students there yet. It would be an excellent field trip for this coming year.

Bob Slingsby has excellent qualifications to teach logging. "This is my 29th year here. Our family was young when we first arrived in Clearwater. Teaching didn't pay enough in those days for us to buy a decent home, so I worked in the bush during the holidays with Dave Tremblay. I also worked with a professional forester for several years, helping with fire-suppression crews," Bob told me.

"One thing we try to teach our students is to utilize every piece of every tree. I teach them how to buck so we get the highest dollar for each log. Everything that comes to the landing must be in a condition to go on the truck and be hauled to the mills. There is no room for excuses or mistakes. I also teach woodworking and drafting."

"You certainly are the right man to be teaching forestry," I replied. "You have a good practical knowledge of what goes on right from the seedling until the tree is manufactured and then further processed into homes and furniture."

Bob went on to give credit to his right-hand man. "The fellow who works with me as field man on this program, Brent Buck, is ideal. He is paid out of the revenue from our log sales. He was a faller for over eight years and also has his own little factory for making custom furniture. When I have to go out in the woods, I can leave him here to handle my classes in the woodworking shop. He is an excellent instructor for these husky young would-be loggers. He's younger and tougher than I am. He also has a brown belt in karate, so the students have all sorts of respect for him whether they're in the shop or out in the woods."

140

Slingsby nicely summarized the thrust of the Clearwater Secondary School Logging Curriculum: "The end use of our timber products, then the nurseries, followed by intensive forestry are going to be the most important factors in the immediate future for our students to study and get involved in. These things must be taught if the industry as we know it today is to survive."

Bob is to be commended for the way he has approached the training and teaching of these future loggers. In my opinion, his safety training alone could well be a lifesaver for any one of them on any given day. There is no substitute for learning the correct and safe way.

His training in woodworking and drafting gives the students an insight into the end use for the logs they have produced. Where they have done commercial thinning, the students can see for themselves the timber growing at an accelerated rate.

In addition, I believe general forestry courses that include the planting and growing of trees should be taught as part of the regular school curriculum. Such education could prevent many of the confrontations that presently take place between industry and the environmentalists. The more young people learn about forests, the better the future will be for all of us.

CHAPTER ELEVEN

Three Clearwater Loggers

"Logging is such a vast industry, with so little time to prepare our young people for it," Bob Slingsby had said. "Many here, like Dave Tremblay, Joe Wadlegger and Ernie Graffunder, help unselfishly by giving their time, and even money if our school program is in a tight spot. These men know the industry inside out. If we didn't have such people, I don't believe we could afford a program like the one we have going here."

Bob was kind enough to introduce me to these three community-spirited Clearwater loggers.

DAVE

Dave Tremblay was waiting in his 4x4 truck to take us up the mountain to his logging operation and see the slash fire that had been lit by the Forest Service the day before, against his advice. Dave was the firewarden for that area and he has been involved with logging all his life. His father and grandfather had logged in the lower Fraser Valley across the river from Chilliwack.

Near the base of the mountain, Dave said, "The area we are looking at to our left has been selectively logged over the last six years by Bob Slingsby's forestry students. They've taken out about 40 loads of logs every year. You're looking at between $45,000 and $50,000 in total revenue. We got this timber at minimum stumpage. That was the deal we made with the B.C. Forest Service. When we thinned the stand six years ago we left only the healthier trees, and some of them have put on almost six inches in diameter since then. You go out here, Joe, and cut one of these trees down and compare the growth rings, and you'll see it's more than double what it was prior to thinning.

"The school's timber came up to about here," Dave said, pointing to a blazed line going off to the west. "In my opinion, the students should do selective thinning on all these prime growing sites. There is plenty of moisture at low elevations on the southern slopes. The biggest of these trees are less than 80 years old. We took out the birch and sold it for firewood, so it wouldn't compete with the fir and pine.

We drove up the logging road for about half a mile, and parked the truck for a better look. "This is what that last stand looked like before we started thinning," Dave explained. "All this area needs commercial thinning, but it's so labour-intensive and expensive that the Forest Service is just letting it grow into a useless thicket.

"By the time you consider unemployment insurance, Canada Pension and holiday pay, it costs between $175 and $200 a day to keep a man in the bush with a power saw. Then you have to add what it costs to get him out to the job and back home again at night. You're looking at about $250 per day," Dave estimated.

"It looks pretty messy by comparison," I agreed.

"The cedar is very poor in this area. The larger trees are nothing more than a bunch of shells. At the 3,000-foot elevation, the best timber is lodgepole pine, which grows to full maturity in about 70 years and is usually clearcut for the simple reason that it grows so thick it's difficult to thin out.

"I'm going to show you several different planted areas as we drive up this logging road. There's one in particular that the government is justly proud of. The trail you see going off to the left is a well-used cross-country ski trail when the snow comes. It's about eight kilometers long and is maintained all winter by the Forest Service. They have a couple of men who keep it groomed. It brings in a lot of skiers, from both Vancouver and Kamloops. Cross-country skiing in this area has become very popular. It's not only good exercise, it gets the people out of the cities and into the woods".

Dave pointed to the left with his right hand. (He'd lost his left arm at the shoulder in a logging accident many years earlier. The Workers' Compensation Board sometimes asks Dave to counsel others who are "up tight" after losing a limb in an accident.) "We're looking at one of the clearcut areas here on the left," he said. "About 90 acres has been replanted. You can see there's plenty of regeneration. The young pine trees are healthy, but they're going to have to do something with all that brush. When a pine forest burns, it usually comes back naturally, and often like gangbusters. I'm going to show you some natural pine higher up that came back after a wildfire four years ago. The 90 acres is solid with young pine trees, some of them already six feet tall.

"That road we see to our left goes to what we call 'The Attorney General's Department' which is actually a minimum security prison. The Attorney General Ministry calls it The Bear Creek Camp. They have a little sawmill up there, Joe, and they cut timbers and bridge-decking for the forestry roads and various other government projects. One paid guy runs the mill. His main purpose is to teach the inmates how to work safely in and around a sawmill."

We could see the timber type starting to change as we got higher up the mountain. "This is Raft Valley and it's quite steep," Dave said. "About 30 percent of the logging in these rougher and steeper areas has to be done with highlead machines."

I asked, "In other words, they're now taking out what was considered inaccessible timber 10 years ago?"

"The whole top side of this mountain burned in a fire started by lightning in the summer of 1973. We'll be getting a good look at it shortly, off to our left. It burned right to the top. We dared not let bulldozers or crews near it when it was burning at its hottest.

"Here we are. This is a natural stand that's come back since '73," my guide and instructor said.

"It looks to be about 80 to 90 percent fir and pine," I suggested.

"As we move along, you'll see there's too much pine in here. This is where the B.C. Forest Service has one of their intensive

144

thinning programs. I believe they took out about three out of every four trees. The stand appears to be doing pretty well right now. That's where that fire went, right up over the top of this mountain. You can see a few old firs that survived the heat. Those old trees would be around 300 years old and, as you can see, they have given off a lot of good seed. Here's the date on this sign: 'Juvenile spacing 1979'. A lot of this spacing is being done by the men and boys from that minimum security camp. We managed to get a guard near the top using bulldozers, so the fire didn't get into the spruce country beyond.

"We patrolled that fire guard night and day for a full month. There was a 30-mile-an-hour wind when the flames roared up to the top of that hill in a matter of two hours. As fires usually do, the growth that comes back makes a good home for wildlife. I can get a nice buck up here any time I need one," Dave said with a grin.

"I came up here shortly after the fire and put this access road in. There were numerous fire-killed, sound cedars that made good fence posts. We salvaged hundreds of them along the roads.

"Here's where a slide came down off the mountain after the fire and buried our new road for some 200 meters with mud, stumps and other debris. It took everything with it.

"This area below the fire was put under the Small Business Forest Enterprise Program. A young fellow who now works for me logged this with horses some 10 years ago. The plan was to go in and take out all those old veteran fir trees before they blew down or died.

"Here's something you should think about," Dave suggested. "If I have a Small Business Licence, I can bid on any or all of the timber sales that come up in the Clearwater District. The big companies will give me up to $22 a cubic metre to bid on any timber sale, but for that they demand first refusal on all the logs produced on those sales at a fair market price. That way, this government's Small Business Forest Enterprise Program is actually controlled by the bigger manufacturing plants. That certainly is not what the small business program was designed to accom-

145

plish. It forces the stumpage prices up so that the average small mill or logger can't afford to buy timber."

"There's the smoke from the slash burning. Now we are getting close to what I'm interested in," I said. "I wanted to get a good look at the way you dispose of all this decadent cedar."

"When we finished logging this area," Dave answered, "there were rotten trees and debris to a depth of 10 feet over most of the area you see burning. All this was tinder dry a week ago, and now all you can see is smoldering stumps and scorched ground.

"The cedar around here is just like powder on the inside. I had two fallers and a bulldozer work here all last summer knocking everything to the ground. When you hit most of these cedars with the Cat blade they just shatter and collapse in a heap.

"The older hemlock is also over 50 percent decayed and rotting. You can see the conks on it, so you know it's finished. I worked by the hour here with two machines and five men all last winter for the B.C. Forest Service. We hauled out what sound hemlock and pine there was for pulp. Then we slashed the cedar and other junk and left it for burning. That's the remains we're looking at here today," Dave explained.

"From an old logger's standpoint, I would say you're putting the adjacent timber in grave danger if the wind should increase," I said. "That could mean big trouble."

"Yesterday morning, they brought in a helicopter and dropped fire balls, starting in the centre and working to the outer edges of the total slash. This creates a horrendous updraft with flames reaching 50 feet in height. Theoretically, this creates a rush of air from the outside in towards the centre. The reason our machines are here is to prevent this fire from spreading.

"I was the fire boss when I advised them not to burn because of a wind warning. Twenty minutes later they set it afire. This is Slocan Forest Product's burning program. There's a forestry officer flying in that helicopter with the Slocan pilot, so the responsibility can go back to the government forestry officer. He's the guy that can say 'yea or nay; burn or don't burn'.

"A little leeway is perhaps tolerable, but the chance of a total disaster happening here is pretty high. We're just hired by Slocan to watch for spot fires that escape after the main slash fires get going, and then put them out with our water tankers.

"In this mountain area here, we've been geared into the cut, burn and run syndrome for some 15 years. Get it down cheap as you can. Rip and tear, rape and pillage, then burn and get the hell out. That seems to be what the two bigger firms with Tree Farm Licences are forcing us to do."

"That may be the thinking of the big outfits," I said, "but it's not the thinking of people like yourself with a family coming on and an interest in the community and its future. I'd like to see an area of younger trees like we just came through properly managed. A few years down the road that could be an ongoing profitable family business. Within 10 years, some of those trees should again be ready for commercial thinning."

"I have three good friends, Joe, who have woodlots and they're just having one hell of a bad time," Tremblay said.

"That's because the government doesn't have the personnel to properly supervise. Woodlots should have certain guidelines and the operator should be able do the rest without interference."

As we neared the top of the mountain, I asked Dave, "In these parts, how much snow would you have on the ground during an average winter?"

"Up to four feet down at the lower elevation. But we logged higher up last winter in as much as nine feet of snow. The block we were working on was a salvage block. The Forest Service wanted us to take the good wood out and then slash the rest and leave it for burning. You'll see, if we can get up there close enough to the fire, that the stumps are cut off eight to 10 feet above the ground in most places. Snowshoes and scoop shovels were part of the fallers' equipment all last winter."

When we were able to get in near the slash fire we could see the central part of the rubbish was cooling down, but the outer edges had flames shooting up over 20 feet. Though the smoke was heavy and thick, it was possible to see most of the burned area

147

which was now about half a mile wide and over two miles long. Dave's Cats were there, building fire breaks. The two skidders, carrying water tanks, were patrolling the edges and his men were putting out spot fires that had jumped the fire guards. The unburned, rotten snags and old useless cedars were being pushed away from the edges toward the centre. The fires had been so hot there were few, if any, of the high stumps left standing.

"This is a pretty clean burn," Dave explained. "Although the slash is black and hot right now, if we don't have a bad wind, this total area should be ready for reseeding or planting by next spring. It's about the only way to get rid of all this old and rotting no good timber. Let's get out of this smoke and heat."

As we went lower on the mountain Dave pointed to another logged area saying, "This is a small clearcut. It's another Small Business Forest Enterprise Program and is one of Joe Wadlegger's sales. Below and to our right there was once some prime red cedar, five to six feet at the stump and as sound as a dollar. I've never seen cedar like it anywhere else in this district. The whole valley bottom also had some beautiful big spruce up to 160 feet tall and four feet in diameter.

Once out of the smoke, Dave continued his guided tour. "Across the river, up in those steeper canyons, there are still a few big cedars left. James Patrick O'Riley owns a small helicopter and hauls shake bolts out of here during the winter. He picks up sling loads of bolts and flies them down to where they can be loaded on trucks. He's nicknamed "Radar." and is quite a character. Some say he can see through the snow! His is a job that requires nerves of steel and plenty of good judgment."

As we drove up the east road, Dave pointed to a plantation of young white pine to our left. For a couple of years Dave had logged white pine and hauled it out to Lumby, an eight-hour round trip, where there is a plant specializing in pine paneling and furniture manufacturing. They soon learned that by falling these brittle trees in two feet or more of snow there was no breakage. Even with that long haul there was good money to be made.

For the last few years, pulp logs were being hauled out to Cache Creek, another day-long return trip. Louisiana Pacific has a barker-chipper plant there and they transport the screened chips directly to their pulp mill in Washington State. Clearwater doesn't have a pulp mill, so there was no demand for this low-grade timber in the immediate district.

"You know, Joe, an area like this is just waste unless it's restocked within 12 months after logging," Dave said.

"The Forest Service here is hiring technicians all the time and it appears we are getting the leftovers. They offer steady employment and pensions and the whole thing, but the opportunity for a bright ambitious young professional forester to advance within the ministry is limited. The only way for advancement is through attrition, no matter how good you are.

"Our District Forester sits in his office most of the time and rarely gets out in the woods to see what's going on. He's a nice gentleman and has done a good job here. But you know all you need is a change of government to throw a monkey wrench into our entire provincial logging policy. It could change things in a matter of weeks, including the staff.

"For the past two summers my son has been supervising the tree planting for Weyerhauser, the huge American outfit. The local ministry office has tried to hire him every summer, but he says no. He feels he would get stuck at some desk job and learn little or nothing about the woods and growing trees. He's getting $3,000 a month as a student with Weyerhauser, but he puts in a lot of long days for that. In the B.C. Forest Service they don't allow overtime. You're on seven hours a day, five days a week. You can't even put yourself through school on that kind of a job."

"We need people like your son to take over a large wood lot or a small Tree Farm Licence, and supervise the whole thing," I said.

"That's his ambition, to be a manager. He's very opinionated and has lots of good ideas. He tells me that once you get within the government guidelines you're handcuffed. If you have any ambition, you are more apt to be pushed down than pushed ahead.

"He's spent some time in Sweden looking at the way they do the job over there, discussing procedures with some of their foresters. You can walk through those Swedish forests where they have logged, and you will see only a few, if any, branches or tops left on the ground. This debris is all bundled and piled along the side of the roads. Then a truck and chipper comes along and chips this material up into small pieces that are sold for domestic heating. This creates employment and there is no reason why it couldn't be done here.

"This road we're on parallels the Raft River for some distance. In this beautiful little Raft Valley, Joe Wadlegger and two local ranchers have grazing leases. Up to 300 beef cattle summer in the area and they do a pretty good job of putting on weight as well as keeping the brush down. Up where we were this morning at the higher levels, they're using sheep to keep the grass under control. This gives the young planted seedlings a better chance to grow. In the Clearwater Forest District there are now 9,000 sheep, several hundred goats and some longhorn cattle being pastured until the fall snow forces them down. At this time of the year the sheep dogs put on a real show.

"This forest district has government funds to assist the sheep ranchers to move their flocks into the newly-planted forests. I've walked over some of the so-called grazing areas and it seems to be working out well. The sheep eat the broadleaf material, such as maple, alder and willow, right down to the size of a pencil. They also keep the tall grass under control. There are a few goats being tried in different areas. They have to keep shepherds with these animals all the time to watch out for predators such as coyotes, dogs and even cougars, which seem to be especially fond of goat or sheep meat!"

It was getting dark when Dave drove up to the camper in the school parking lot. After supper I headed for a meeting Dave had set up for me with Ernie Graffunder.

ERNIE

Ernie Graffunder has done it all.

He's been the smallest of all gyppos, taking out cedar telephone poles. All he needed was a good axe, one horse, a peavey to manhandle the poles, and one crosscut saw. Massive doses of energy and determination were also needed to make money logging poles.

There were no sawmills buying logs in the Clearwater District, so he cut, trimmed and hauled the poles to the railroad siding, then loaded them on rail cars. Siglet from Vernon was the big contractor, and he bought all the longer poles, 50 feet and over which needed special flat cars and a special market. The shorter poles were sold locally.

"Us young guys would find and buy little pockets of cedar here and there and that was the way we made a few bucks. Those long poles were a bonus. Without an established contractor we could never have handled them," Ernie said. "I was only 13 years old."

"They'll probably go back to horses when they start thinning some of their planted timber stands," I suggested. "Maybe not a horse, maybe some little machine yet to be invented that can skid out the thinnings without packing down the soil, or damaging the remaining trees. Something with wide, low pressure tires that swivel in any direction."

"You've got the right idea there, Joe," he agreed.

"Actually, the Forest Service has recently sold some horse-logging sales around here," Ernie said. "I'm sure that's a step in the right direction. I've often thought of approaching our district forester about selectively pre-logging the cedar poles in some of our logging areas. The way it is now, most of the pole-sized cedar trees just get knocked over, smashed up and wasted."

When he couldn't find more pole timber, Ernie spent some 30 years as logging superintendent for Clearwater Timber Products. That was before the quota system was put into effect in the early '50s. It was his responsibility to locate and buy timber in the Adams River country east of Kamloops, and do most of the cruising and layout work necessary to put up timber sales and establish quotas. "It was interesting work," he said, "and required all sorts of negotiating with the government forestry people and other officials.

"I took early retirement five years ago in 1985 and started my own logging company," Ernie explained. "It's better to get out on your own. You don't have to punch the clock every morning and then listen to some young college graduate tell you how to log. When I did government work I would listen if there was time, but I didn't always carry out their ideas, especially when I knew they were way off in left field."

Ernie logs with two fairly new Cats and one rubber-tired skidder. He also does contract work for the B.C. Department of Highways, and takes contracts building roads for other logging companies. He does site preparation for tree planting. During the late fall he's kept busy fire guarding and slash burning for the Forest Service.

"Then we got into cattle ranching. That seems to be what most old loggers like us do when they get past 60. I'm 64 and everybody wants to know what I'll do in retirement. I've no intention of retiring for at least another 10 years. We're raising some registered Simmental cattle and my two sons and daughter look after the ranching jobs. Most of our cows and the herd bull are purebred stock. There's a ready market here for good beef animals.

"In Clearwater, ranching is a borderline proposition at best, but if you have a woodlot to go along with it, both businesses become stable.

"I've always believed that the worst thing that could ever happen to me is to have nothing to do. I'd probably go crazy in no time," said Ernie with a big grin.

"I've made several applications for woodlots, but I've not been successful in getting one," Ernie said. "We were advised that one was going to be put up for sale this year in our timber district. It was near our land so I definitely was going to try and get it. It was about 1,100 acres. Big enough for any average family.

"We already own about 700 acres of timber land, and about two-thirds of that is already planted and growing. We planned to put the two areas together when, and if, the government approved our application. We already have the necessary equipment and a good knowledge of the local climate and logging procedures.

"I also have the necessary quota, although it doesn't amount to much right now. About 17 loads a year. That's not enough in itself, but it did establish us in this forest district as a logging operator during the 1950s. I ended up with a quota because we were logging on timber sales at the time they started the quota system. Anyone having an active timber sale or sales at the time was allotted a quota in the Clearwater Forest District."

When I had interviewed Ernie Graffunder he was confident he would get the logging rights to the nearby woodlot. There was no opposition from his neighbours and he had worked out his logging plan, done all the paperwork, and was waiting for the B.C. Forest Service to announce that applications would be considered.

Nothing happened, and finally, months later, he drove into Clearwater from his ranch at Vavenby, 12 miles east, and asked, "What's up, fellows?"

He was told the B.C. Forest Service was not issuing any woodlot rights in the Clearwater area. This did not make sense to him. Family-operated woodlots was the way of the future and would bring more prosperity and employment to the area, as well as increasing the timber cut and improving reforestation, and better management of the forests.

He was told that it was a matter of the Forest Service being understaffed in his district and there was no manpower available to inspect and approve applications.

"But I'm confident it will come," he told me months later. "I can wait. It has to come. This is the way it has to go. I'm convinced of that. It's only common sense."

So, while the Graffunder family waits, Ernie continues to work on providing input for the Forest Resources Commission which he sees as a big plus to the future of our forests.

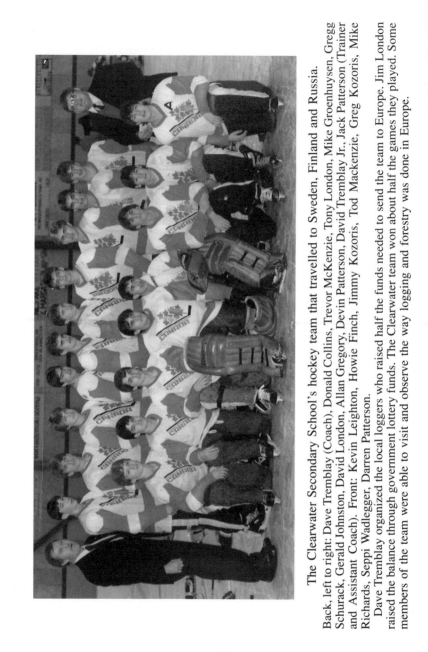

The Clearwater Secondary School's hockey team that travelled to Sweden, Finland and Russia. Back, left to right: Dave Tremblay (Coach), Donald Collins, Trevor McKenzie, Tony London, Mike Groenhuysen, Gregg Schurack, Gerald Johnston, David London, Allan Gregory, Devin Patterson, David Tremblay Jr., Jack Patterson (Trainer and Assistant Coach). Front: Kevin Leighton, Howie Finch, Jimmy Kozoris, Tod Mackenzie, Greg Kozoris, Mike Richards, Seppi Wadlegger, Darren Patterson.

Dave Tremblay organized the local loggers who raised half the funds needed to send the team to Europe. Jim London raised the balance through government lottery funds. The Clearwater team won about half the games they played. Some members of the team were able to visit and observe the way logging and forestry was done in Europe.

154

"The big companies still don't care. They're still doing things the same old way, the way they want to do them. The big guys don't care about the communities.

"It's us little guys in the district that have the concerns for the future of our land, our forests and our communities and we can do the job better than the big companies."

"It's just a matter of time until the government will have to recognize the value of families like yourselves. Then you will get your chance to continue doing the thing you do best," I said.

"Meanwhile, we'll be staying, just as we always have," Ernie said.

"There have been a lot of people wanting to buy my quota, but it's not for sale. Without it, we have little or no hope of ever getting a woodlot licence. Both my sons are prepared to go in with me," Ernie said proudly.

"Well, Ernie, I'm sure there's nothing more beneficial to a family than to have forest land they can manage themselves. Then, when you plant a tree, you're planting it for the family's future. You're planting it for your grandchildren or your great grandchildren. The family can feel secure and look forward to the next hundred years at least. Right now, there's little or no security in the timber business for our young people. Everything is changing at such a rate, most people are nervous about getting deeply involved financially."

"That's right," Ernie said. "I agree with you absolutely. I've always argued that the reason we have so many problems with our young people is because it's taking too long to get that next crop planted and growing. There could be no greater deed than to leave something permanent and secure for our future generations. It doesn't matter if it's a family group or a limited company. Each one will own so many shares representing so many acres of timber land. When they get too old or want to retire, they can sell their shares to any member of the limited company or family on a first refusal basis. That's where us older folks with experience and knowledge can be of some help. It's so important to get things started in a proper manner.

155

"We have a patch of timber on the hillside back there," Ernie gestured with his arm. "When I bought that 160 acres in 1945, it cost me $350. A Christmas tree company offered me $500 for the privilege of cutting the Christmas trees that same fall. I politely rejected their offer. It would do your heart good to walk through that patch of timber today. It's ready to be commercially thinned for the second time. We have actually grown two forest crops in 45 years. If proper thinning is done every 10 years or so, the yield can be more than double the original timber stand over a 50-year period. The licensees on the big Tree Farms have been talking about planting but doing little or nothing about it. It's bordering on crinimal negligence," Ernie believes.

"Most of the better growing sites here could be thinned or selectively logged," I suggested.

"There's nothing wrong with that, Joe, provided the remaining stand of trees are left wind safe. This is very important, you know. In some areas, the tree roots don't grow deep enough. You start to thin or take out a portion of the stand and a big wind comes along and whoosh, it blows the rest over. It takes plenty of experience to recognize this.

"I was talking to Danny Moss. He has a woodlot and the Forest Service people insisted that he go in and selectively log this area. The next spring, a wind came along and flattened all the remaining trees. If that's what we train and educate our Registered Professional Foresters for, we had better get them some experience or get rid of them. They must know what they are doing, not guess at it.

"If you knew the amount of wood I've seen wasted or burned in the last 30 years, Joe, I'm telling you straight, you wouldn't want to believe it. There was never a thought of ever being short of timber in the 1930s. We're now looking at no more than 20 to 25 years of first-growth timber. I can show you an area up in the Otter Creek Valley that was harvested in the '50s. There are second-growth trees there over 60 feet tall and more than 12 inches at the base and growing like crazy.

"This Clearwater country is generally recognized as having some of the better growing areas in the entire province. This is where the government should be concentrating on more wood-lots. Little guys doing their own thing. Instead of having a couple of big guys, they should have 50 to 100 of the local people growing trees. There's plenty of room, and the district could double its present production. The concept of woodlots would give the local families and private citizens permanent employment, and there would be stability for our towns and communities.

"The big companies will never be able to get their people to have the same dedicated interest as the private owners of wood-lots. You always look after what is your own better.

"For instance, if a wildfire got going up on our sidehill near the timber at, say, two o'clock some summer morning, the whole family, the neighbours, everybody would be up there with buckets, bulldozers and tank trucks. We'd have the fire out before it had time to get really going. There would always be capable people right here to protect our future crops. If we had real trouble controlling a fire, we'd just call more of our neighbours." Ernie said.

"Most people in the big companies are mostly concerned about their pay cheques that come along every two weeks. There surely has to be more than that to life.

"If our young people can look down the road and say, 'Look, I can see my grandchildren running this mill and growing enough trees to keep it going' that would be great. The parcel of land that I have up here is a real good example. I can show my kids what can happen in a lifetime. I was only 20 years old when I bought that first piece of land. I was born in 1926, so I've seen some hard times and also some good times.

"When I was a kid, and we wore the feet out of our socks, mother just cut the bottoms off and knit new feet onto them. When our woollen underwear got ragged, any places that weren't completely worn out she'd unravel, and then used that wool yarn to knit our sweaters and mittens."

"You must have come up in about the same kind of family I did," I told him. "How many were in your family?"

"Ten; four boys, six girls."

"We had ten, too. Five boys, five girls. I believe we are both lucky to have grown up in such families. I'm positive that a family business, well, like the woodlots we're talking about, can build strong families. The multinationals should be allowed to buy the logs produced on woodlots at competitive prices in an open market. But never the land. Never. Never. The land must always remain with the people who live there."

"The way our youngsters are flocking to the cities, Joe, there's not even going to be standing room for them. You know, I can't understand why or how anybody can live in those infernal cities. It'd drive me crazy. I go to Vancouver about once a year on business and that's enough for me."

Ernie recalled one trip he made to the big city. "When Tom Waterland was the Social Credit Minister of Forests, I went to see him in Victoria. I suggested that if he really wanted this woodlot concept, this family-type operation to take hold, he should start at the bottom and straighten out the taxes. The ranchers are not going to put their land into timber if the heavy tax on wild land is going to defeat their purpose. You must make sure tree farm land stays as ranch land for tax purposes. At that time there were two different classes. I went into this in depth with the powers-that-be in Kamloops. They insisted that if you put your land into a woodlot, it gets classed as wild or woodlot land. But as far as I know, they've changed their mind and are now leaving it as ranch land and it's being taxed at that lower rate. I like to believe that my efforts were responsible for keeping the taxes in line.

"We spend every fall on site preparation with our two Cats. The land must be made ready for spring planting. Just like the wheat farmers do. But I'm talking seedlings. We've made our share of mistakes, especially at the higher elevations, planting the wrong species in the wrong place at the wrong time of year. Things like that. But we're learning. It's going to take more than one generation to learn good forestry and tree growing.

158

"Then there's another thing that can be unpredictable—the weather. You can have the finest site preparation and do the best possible job of planting, but if it doesn't rain for six weeks in early summer, tough luck. A lot of those little seedlings will shrivel up and die. Then, again, get a bad early fall frost, and many more of them can freeze. There are any number of things that can set them back or kill them.

"A lot of the people who are trying to tell us what to do have little or no long-term practical experience whatsoever when it comes to growing a new forest. They're just out of university and are full of theory and good intentions. Yet, these are the people responsible for our future forests.

"One of the best things the Forest Service guys have done here was to start what they call a Public Advisory Committee. I'm on it. They don't meet in the summer because everyone's too busy, but they hold meetings twice a month all winter. They have good attendance at these meetings. Our committee believes a woodlot should be 1,000 acres or more to be economically feasible. Actually, a 1,000 acres around here will give you an annual allowable cut of about 1,225 cubic metres. That's 30 to 35 truck loads. Not bad. In fact, pretty good.

"The Clearwater Timber Company was a family company at one time. But you know, things happen. Now it's been taken over by a Spokane group and they seem to have little or no feeling for the community's future. It's a shame. They are currently cutting far more timber on their Tree Farm Licence than they are growing. It's just a matter of time until they run out of timber, if they keep it up."

"Ernie, I believe that a district like Clearwater can never fail if it follows your ideas, but a town with only one big company can fail overnight. Just shut the mill down, and that's it."

"Yes, Joe, I was very happy when the provincial government announced it was going to at least double the number of woodlots in the province. But, so far, at least, they haven't done much about it."

159

"I wrote up a brief for our District Forester last year. One of my complaints was they are allowing clearcutting continuously and not leaving enough seed blocks to start a new crop. I can show you where, up on some of these mountains there's mile after mile of clearcut with nothing left in between. Not a tree to provide seed for the clearcut. Originally it was to be only 50 percent cut at one time by any harvesting system. I can show you mountains that are absolutely bare, wiped out 20 years ago. *No regeneration. No replanting. No nothing.*

"There's another reason, Joe, why they're doing all this clearcutting. It's a valid reason, but you've got to stop and think about it. This is mostly overmature and decadent timber at the higher elevations. They're trying to salvage as much as they can before it falls down or rots. This is quite reasonable, providing they burn and replant that same year."

"Did you ever think of a clearcut and a burn, then white Dutch clover seeded over it before planting the seedlings?" I asked. "It doesn't die off, it puts the proper nutrients back into the soil. What's more, it stops the weeds from growing in so quickly. This clover rarely grows high enough to flatten the young trees when the snow comes. It could feed the deer, elk, moose, grouse, geese, rabbits. At the same time, it prevents erosion."

Ernie answered, "To the best of my knowledge, it wouldn't create competition for the young trees. Some of those other high-growing grasses fall over with the first snowfall and bend the young seedldings down with it. If they do survive, about all those bent trees will be good for is making hockey sticks. Dutch clover won't do that. Up in the sunny alpine or semi-alpine country you don't have to seed anything. The natural growth comes in and competes with what's there. That's where you need to bring in the cattle or sheep to knock the weeds back."

He looked around and out the window and said, "We can always make a good family living around here. We've got a good garden. We can trap fur in the winter. We can cut a few trees when we need extra cash. We've got our cattle and we can catch fish in the rivers."

160

"That boy you see in this picture is a journeyman millwright," Ernie said proudly, passing me a picture of one of his sons. "Another son of mine is a heavy duty licensed mechanic. The third one is a ticketed welder. Our daughter is a professional cook. Boy, can she cook," Ernie bragged.

"And you've got about the finest combination you could ever wish for to run a woodlot, do the logging, and you could even have your own sawmill to cut added-value lumber," I suggested.

Then, offhandedly, he gave me a tip I'd never heard of in my 82 years in, around and about the logging and lumbering industry. He spoke about Christmas trees. "You put a blaze near the bottom of the tree. That stunts it and makes it bush out. Some of the best Christmas trees in the world are grown that way. When you cut this tree, you don't cut it off at ground level. You leave it up about waist high with some branches, preferably about three good healthy branches and these branches will turn up. In four to five years you've got another three good Christmas trees. How about that!,"

Ernie Graffunder is typical of the proud, independent small logger. Men like Ernie, Dave Tremblay and Joe Wadlegger are the foundation of good logging practices. Their experience, knowledge and concerns for the land, forest and community are invaluable.

It was well past midnight when we had our last cup of tea and hit the sack. In bed I thought, "You put a blaze at the bottom of . . . "

Joe Wadlegger with a typical load of logs.

Joe with a special order of bridge timbers from his mill.

JOE

The following morning, September 19, 1990, I drove 10 miles east of Clearwater to look over Joe Wadlegger's logging and milling operations. He was by his small, tidy sawmill in his lumber yard selecting newly-cut special bridge timbers for one of his customers.

Joe's mill had burned down the previous year and he'd just finished rebuilding it, making it the only added-value sawmill in the Clearwater district.

"There was no insurance on the old mill," Joe said. "Right away we ordered new specialized machinery and began building. It was expensive but we were able to pay for the whole thing by borrowing from the bank. This mill employs up to 14 people when the loggers are counted. It provides them and their families with a good living. I'm grateful we can keep it going steadily. It is a stable part of our community and our family is very proud of it."

Joe is pleased that his 19-year-old son Hans is following in his footsteps. He is the woods foreman and is also keenly interested in the sawmill. He has already completed a course in heavy duty mechanics. His older son Joseph, known as Seppi, is taking forestry courses in Prince George, and intends to eventually graduate as a Registered Professional Forester so he can submit and sign working plans, or supervize woodlots. Joe's eldest child Elizabeth graduated from York University in Toronto and is now married. His youngest daughter Barbara was attending Clearwater Secondary School.

His wife Hazel's family were trappers and moved to Clearwater from North Dakota in the 1920s. Hazel has spent all of her life in the Valley. She handles all of the book-work and is a great help to her husband.

Joe was born in Obervellacha in Austria in 1935 on the family farm. "My dad had taken over the farm from his dad," Joe explained. "My grandfather's will stated that every child was to get 200 cubic meters of timber. Not cash. When they married, if they wanted the money, they could negotiate. We were not allowed to sell to an outsider so the farm could not be divided. The next generation must always have the opportunity to buy it. So when I left for Canada, my portion stayed in the family. Four of the children wanted to build their own homes, so they took the timber. They carefully logged the trees themselves and took them to a sawmill nearby where they had them cut into lumber.

"We had an old sawmill my grandfather had built. When we came home from school we had to stack the lumber. The mill only cut about 10 logs a day, but we learned, and it was a lasting education. We cut precisely what our customer wanted and nothing was ever wasted.

"As a kid, I started out using a cross-cut saw with my dad. We had to go up the steep parts at the back where we had our own forest and climb around the rocks to find that special tree we wanted. Then we'd let ourselves down over the bluffs with ropes and cut it down. To us, this was fun.

"Austria is small and so are the farms, but on our 60-acre farm we kept a team of logging horses as well as some cattle. Trees were handled the same way as when my dad was a kid. When we cut down a tree, three small ones were planted the same year to take its place. That's the way we were taught. The European way.

"If you're planting in an area with moss on the floor, you only open up small patches, just enough so the young trees can see sunlight. You left the moss around the seedling and in two or three years there was a beautiful timber crop growing. In the places where you have done a good job of planting, there's a healthy re-growth and you feel very proud.

"We actually looked forward to going tree planting every spring. It was a family outing—like a picnic. In the poor areas we were taught to pick a spot where we knew the young tree would have the best chance of growing. We bought our seedlings from a private nursery about a mile down the road. Only seed from native trees was used. It's still done that way. Forestry was taught in our schools. It's in the blood of our people.

"Before I left home to come out to Canada, my dad sat me down and gave me some good advice: 'Work for yourself if you have the chance. Whatever you start, stick with it. Try to buy some timber and land for a farm.' If I gave that up now I'd have to go to work for some big lumber company and punch a clock.

"That's what makes Canada so great—the space and the freedom. I've never been sorry I came here. When people come to visit us from my homeland they are amazed when they see what we have.

"'Look at all that land, look at what you guys still have here. The space. The trees. The cleared pastures and the mountains, even your own sawmill,' they exclaim. Then pointing up to the logged area, they ask, 'Who lives up there?'

"'Nobody lives up there,' I reply. 'It's a clearcut. We've logged that area, and it's all been replanted. That will be our new crop of timber in about 30 years.'"

So Joe's understanding of reforestation is deeply ingrained in the European tradition.

"The Forest Service here seems to come out about every year or so with some new type of experiment they want us to try out. That's why we've been clearcutting here for the last five or six years. That's the killer right now as far as I see it. In Austria we handle our timber area the same as farm land. Every spring we walk over it and look at the trees. If a seedling planted last year didn't grow, we try to analyze the reasons why and then replace it. Maybe it was a spruce planted in a place where a pine or fir should have been.

"In Austria, farming and forestry is one industry, under one ministry. The forests there have every size of tree in one stand, from the little ones right up to mature trees. They rarely ever clearcut. The protection from wind is there so the trees are not as exposed. We've been doing it that way for generations. My family has been on the same land for 500 years. We were never allowed to rob the forest by taking everything out. Grandfather wouldn't hear of it.

"This is why we had trouble above our farm last year. The owner had clearcut the creek bottom all the way up the sidehill. It was only a small creek, but when the rains came it flooded. The needles and branches piled up and then got washed on down to the next level. It built up a little more each time it moved until there was a dam with a small lake behind it. When that broke half the sidehill slid away. In Europe you'd have the neighbours on your neck if you tried that."

"When I came to Canada and saw all those trees and all that land, it really shocked me to see the wastefulness and hear the outcry about the dwindling forests. What can we do? What has to be done? To me it seemed obvious. Everyone must learn to grow trees. The industry here cannot keep going with just speed and big volumes. Whatever they cut must be replaced at once with young healthy seedlings."

"This is why I'm here, to learn from people like you," I said, "to encourage people to try for that sort of stability in our forests. If a family has land and trees they can be self-sufficient."

"But here in Clearwater we are spoiled," Joe said. "When I first came here in 1959 I started logging with a good team of horses. I hadn't forgotten my dad's words, so I always worked on contract, never by the hour. All I had to do was cut the trees down, then take two 18-foot logs off the butt and the rest of the tree was left in the bush to rot or be burned. I suppose it was economics, but, coming from a place where every stick down to two inches was peeled and used, I couldn't believe the waste. Within a few years I was contracting with Clearwater Timber Products to clear and log their right-of-ways.

"In Europe if a log is over a certain size and of good quality, it has a higher stumpage price. Here they charge on volume. I believe a tree farmer should only be allowed to log as much timber as his land will produce each year, and should consult with a Registered Professional Forester before logging on areas that need special care.

"When I first came here, the big companies were just starting to hire private contractors to do their logging. When I bought my first logging trucks Dave Tremblay did the yarding and loading.

"In some cases there would be 30 to 40 percent of what I thought was usable wood either lying on the ground or left standing. At that time there was no pulp mill within trucking distance. The local sawmill wouldn't take any hemlock, birch, poplar or small fir. The Forest Service didn't ask to us take this type of timber out, so it blew down and rotted away. All that waste is one of the main reasons we're becoming short of timber today."

Joe Wadlegger believes there is enough timber around Clearwater to sustain the volume they're presently cutting for at least 50 years. By then, with intensive forestry the new crop should be sufficiently grown to log or comercially thin for the second time. If it's good for 50 years, providing they learn how to grow trees, it can go on forever.

"At one time, I was the only private land owner in this whole valley who reforested after the timber was logged. All our land is planted right back to the highest boundary. We've had beautiful recovery. Some of those trees that need thinning are already big enough to be logged for pulp. It's about one of the best growing areas in the Clearwater district.

"Anyone who logs should have to replant the same year. In Europe you do not pay taxes on timbered land—you pay stumpage when you harvest it. This is how they encourage the growing of trees.

"When we got our first timber sale, it started out as a game protection area. Later, when the B.C. Forest Service saw how well it was working, they turned it into what they called a 'forest demonstration area'. We were happy to go along with it, and now they are sending people up here by the dozens to see how it should be done. It was basically a special thinning and replanting program, much like I was taught by my dad. In Europe, they clearcut only on some of the steeper land where it's unsafe to log by any other method.

"One of our local foresters looked over an area where I had been logging. He ordered me to burn. Within an hour of lighting it a wind came up and that fire got out of control, burning over 2,000 acres of virgin timber. But if you go back there today you'll see a beautiful stand of uniform timber because all that burned area was planted the following year. They've done several thinnings, and there are places up in the higher elevations where you already have trees ten inches at the stump and 50 feet tall.

"When the Forest Service changed its cutting size in 1965 from a 14-inch to an 8-inch stump, we had to go back over several hundred hectares again to log everything down to the 8-inch size. This was a good and necessary change for the Clearwater district.

"Another change I'd like to see is cooperation in tree-planting. I would gladly go for a week tree-planting for a neighbour. Then the neighbour could come to my place and do the same for me. That's the way it is in Austria. Nobody wants or needs to do tree planting the whole year round. Planting should only be done when the conditions are right.

"In 1990, the Weyerhauser Company hired school boys. They had a huge area to plant and the kids naturally got bored and started putting bunches of seedlings in stump holes, or hiding them. Then they'd say they had planted so many trees and get paid for them. This could not happen with proper supervision.

"I'm not running the companies down. But if they want to have a second forest they're going to have to put people out there planting who will do the job properly. What would be wrong if the mill shut down for a week or two and let the crew go tree planting. That would give assurance their children will have timber and jobs in the future. It's one more argument for wood lots run by families."

"Well, it's good to see there's finally somebody here who can cut good lumber and specialty timbers for the local market," I said, looking at his two-story sawmill, built along European lines.

"I don't as yet have a barker and chipper. I'm sure it won't be long before we have to put out some pretty big dollars to buy that expensive machinery. There's no way out of it, if we are to produce chips for the pulpmill near Kamloops and use our poorest timber rather than waste it," Joe Wadlegger explained.

"Well, you're sure making a good job of cutting lumber and timbers. It's quality production," I said.

"We have no trouble getting our price. We have as many orders as we can handle. We do a good job and give the best service possible and it pays off.

"I can see lots of opportunities here for my two sons. One is already our logging manager, doing the welding and making repairs. The other will soon finish his forestry course. Both have been over to Europe several times so they have a good understanding of added-value products and about growing trees.

"We sometimes have trouble getting enough logs of the right size for the specialized orders, so I get into quite a few arguments here with the Forest Service."

"Your two sons Hans and Seppi should each be applying for a woodlot to make it more of a family business, with more timber," I suggested.

"Woodlots are a real good thing. A woodlot is usually 300 to 400 acres, which is a good size, and it's usually in a growing stage, meaning already stocked with some of the trees ready to cut. There are real economic benefits there. I've already got about 1,000 acres in timber. I haven't put it all in timber. There has to be enough room for the mill and a lumber yard. I also have a bit of it in hay for cattle. Having grown up on a farm it's only natural to want some good beef animals around. Anyway, this land was partly logged when I bought it. There was only about 200 hectares in timber. We keep thinning the bigger trees out and now have a beautiful stand of timber right above our mill. We planted all the logged land with the kids when they were little. My wife, the whole family was involved. We didn't go at it day in and day out. We'd plant maybe two or three thousand trees at a time.

"Even when my dad was getting old, I remember if we didn't plant a tree properly, the way he was taught, we had to dig it up. He'd tell us to dig a narrow little hole, find a good sized cow turd and put that into the hole, then mix it with the soil before we put in the young tree. That was getting the job done right in his opinion. When we explain this to some of the local people they just laugh. But when they go up and see big healthy trees it's funny to see how serious they get.

"I keep at this business because my boys seem interested in carrying on. I don't want it for myself. Doing it for them is my satisfaction. I want to pass something on to the next generation."

I said, "This type of outlook will result in sustained yield. It's about the only thing that will."

"I have a strong feeling," Joe said, "that no matter what political changes take place, what the big companies do, the little guy can do it better. He's got to be able to plan and see a future. He's got to be determined and he's got to be given the freedom to do most things his own way."

CHAPTER TWELVE

Two-Row Wampum

When we drove into Lillooet, we chatted briefly with Chief Roger Adolph of the Fountain Indian Band. He is a chief by election and he is also a member of the hereditary chief family. The previous chief was his uncle.

He told us about "The two-row wampum, a beaded belt that was the first treaty symbol between the native people in Canada and the settlers. It started with the Six Nations Confederacy—the Iroquois Confederacy—where the treaties between the different members of the confederacy were in the form of these wampum belts. The information was put down in a coded form with beads on a belt, and that was the basis of the treaty. There are two parallel rows of beads that represent two canoes going down a river beside each other. They never run into each other because they're going side by side in the same direction all the time.

If somebody wanted to get out of one canoe and into the other canoe, he had to remove his clothes so that he didn't carry any of his own culture, language, or anything, over from one canoe to the other. The two-row wampum symbolizes that native people and non-native people can be together on the same land without necessarily having to be subordinate one to the other.

The chief explained the difference between the native's concept of land ownership and the fee-simple concept that the non-native person uses.

"When we say this is our land, what we mean is that we are responsible for this land. We don't mean we own it in the way a non-native person owns a piece of land."

He said he felt ashamed that the natives have not looked after the land as the Great Spirit expected them to do.

"Our own people have not been exercising their responsibility. Even if looking after it means not letting anyone else spoil it." He talked about native people wanting a role in planning the use of the land.

In his younger years, Roger Adolph was a professional boxer. He travelled around England for a while as an Indian boxer, so he knows the white world fairly well. Chief Adolph feels that not only do the native people speak a different language, but the way they express themselves is different. In the native world they never take positions just for the sake of bargaining; they are straightforward. He feels he has learned how to function with the white man's way of speaking almost as well as in his own language. Some things he finds difficult or impossible to explain without using his native way of speaking.

While we were talking to him he was waiting to be called as a witness to the trial of someone who was being charged with uttering threats to a policeman. He didn't go into detail, but basically he felt that it was simply a misunderstanding of the different ways of speaking.

He did explain about talking to loggers who are unhappy about the waste and the way logging is done. He says many of his own people are loggers and they invariably say that they're not happy with the way the work is done.

He feels very strongly that the management of the land has to be the management of all of the resources together. He is sure that if the deer, the grouse, the hikers, the tourists, the skiers, the birds, the whole lot are taken into consideration, they can put this thing together without too much of a problem.

"Keep it simple and fair," is the way he closed our interview.

After talking with Chief Adolph I met with Dr. Trevor Chandler, a man who has learned to live side-by-side with native people.

I interviewed Trevor at his home in Lillooet overlooking the great gorge of the silt-laden Fraser River about 100 miles north and west of Vancouver. Here in his office, surrounded by computers and books, he prepares his lectures in biology and ecology for the Open University of B.C.

Trevor Chandler was born in England, but he grew up in the mountains where he now lives. In 1965, he graduated from the University of Guelph, in Ontario, with a Bachelor of Science degree in agriculture. He then earned his Ph.D. in plant physiology and ecology at Simon Fraser University.

Dr. Chandler has worldwide experience in research, management and consulting. He spent nine years in the tropics, mostly in Africa, in agricultural and environmental systems research, including assignments with CUSO (was Canadian Universities Services Overseas), Canadian International Development Agency and the Food and Agriculture Organization of the United Nations. He was the first technical development officer in the newly-established (1977) International Council for Research in Agroforestry, the world's first international agroforestry organization, set up to examine the problems of tropical forests.

Since his return to Lillooet in 1980, he has worked as an independent consultant on a wide range of agricultural, land use and environmental impact projects, including many for local native groups.

Dr. Chandler is the founder and president of Landscope Consulting Corporation, a company that deals primarily in project and natural resources management and sustainable development planning. Landscope works on projects involving land use, environmental concerns and community affairs in rural, small and medium-sized community settings.

Landscope's Vancouver office is headed by partner Jim Norie, a civil engineer who specializes in housing development assistance, physical development planning and community economic development. His experience includes completing a park master plan for Calgary and later becoming that city's first environmental planner. Jim has also participated in the feasibility and master planning of two ski areas.

As we sat around the dinner table that evening, my first question was, "Are we raping our land here in British Columbia, or are we really trying to set up a management system to produce 'Forests Forever' as the big companies' advertising campaign calls it?"

"What we're talking about is the concept of sustainability, Joe. If we want sustainable forestry, we should start doing it now and be willing to pay the price."

"One of our major problems seems to be that everyone isn't treated equally," I remarked. "There is one set of standards for the gyppos, the small operators, and another for the larger Tree Farm Licences."

"Well, if they're talking about sustainable forestry, they should all be doing it. As long as we have government, and this is one of its purposes, it should ensure that everybody operates within the same set of standards. Then the person who does good forestry doesn't get penalized economically. The companies that don't practise good forestry should lose their right to harvest timber on public lands."

"You mean those that don't practise good forestry should have to pay or lose their timber?" I asked.

"Right now, these are the people who make the most money because they get away with it. We've had what is called 'sympathetic administration', where the government was deliberately allowing forest companies not to meet their standards. The standards are low enough already.

"Have you seen the new Pre-Harvest Prescription forms that, theoretically, have to be processed and approved by a B.C. Ministry of Forests official before logging can begin?" he asked me.

"You mean on timber sales, or on Tree Farm Licences?" I responded.

"I believe on both. The number of topics they cover is fairly comprehensive, but some tend to be shallow," he said.

"Why do you say that? Are they recommending a certain type of thinning, or what?"

"No," he replied. "the purpose of the Pre-Harvest Silviculture Prescription (PHSP) is to be sure a Registered Professional Forester has a chance to have a look at the area and review the decisions on how the forest is going to be re-established before permission is given to go ahead and start logging.

"One of the problems is that this administrative process doesn't require anyone to look at all the land use alternatives and then choose the best. I've never seen a PHSP in which the management objective goes beyond mere timber removal. I believe there should be some major changes made in which the total land use is properly assessed, taking into account agriculture, tourism, parks, ecology, fish, water quality and wildlife values, grazing rights and a fair settlement of any native land claims over an area. The sooner this more complete approach is taken, the better it will be for all of us."

"Well, the Forests Ministry certainly seems to be losing ground at an alarming rate, as far as a sustained forestry yield is concerned," I agreed.

"The Forests Ministry has at least taken the first step by requiring the PHSPs. In theory, unless you have completed one, you're not allowed to cut. At least this forces you to think about the process of how you're going to get the forest growing again before you can go in there and cut. The problem is that the process doesn't require you to look at all the different alternatives and then choose the best one. It simply requires you to put forward one that's been signed by an RPF. Then the government says it's okay.

"But I don't think the Forests Ministry is going to vigorously question what's on the form, or go out and inspect the woods to ensure that what is on it is actually what's being carried out. At least they haven't done this to date. They don't have enough staff.

"When the cutbacks occurred a few years ago, the decision was that they were supposed to check up on 10 percent of the logging activity. In other words, 90 percent would likely not get inspected. Can we be sure that the 10 percent that does get exam-

175

ined will be chosen at random? Or will government inspectors be told which ones to check?"

"Have you got any definite ideas on a land claim settlement plan with the natives?" I asked. "You are pretty close to the bands here, around Lillooet."

"Settling the Indian land claims is one of the first things our provincial government must do before it can ever get into intensive forest management. Government has to know how much, and what land it is going to have to manage. And then it has to take in all aspects of land use."

Dr. Chandler believes there are two ways to look at intensive forest management. One is, as far as B.C. is concerned, that not a very high percentage of the timbered land is going to be suitable for intensive forestry in the first place. He says intensive forest management is similar to good agriculture. Only the best-producing land should be intensively managed. These high-producing areas will give the highest return for the money and effort put into them. He believes that it's not cost-effective to intensively manage the poorer sites, or likely even the medium sites. It's bad land use management for companies or governments to try to intensively farm those areas for trees; it is not only uneconomical, but to say you're going to do it is 'living a lie.' You don't manage the poorer sites, you mine them. You just take the timber off with no intention to really manage. You must at least leave enough seed trees in order to get a new crop started naturally.

"One example is a site in the middle of the Stein Valley, where there are 97-year old trees that are only big enough to use as tent poles. If we go in there and take out the bigger timber, or clearcut an area like that, we are not creating a sustainable yield situation. Sustainable yield isn't a concept that makes sense to us in scales of 500 years; 500 years is 20 generations. We can't sensibly talk about sustainable management on the scale of so many generations. In our culture, there's simply no memory over that length of time.

"If we're going to do sustainable management on poor sites then, in my view, what we've got to say is that we're going to leave that site in its natural state. We should calculate, depending on the present growth increment, how much can be taken out every 20 years in order to keep the area in a healthy state. We have to learn to accept that what we can take out right now is what will grow back by itself in 20 years. If we can decide that, then we might be able to develop a sustainable management system for that piece of land.

"To talk about 'conversion', that is to take all the old trees off and let new growth come in, in terms of sustainable management, is a lie, because it's going to be up to 500 years before we get back to anything like an equivalent forest.

"That would be one good formula," I said. "It would be like good farming. Assess what you can harvest now that will recover in one generation."

"I would prefer to plan over five years," he said, "but that means we'd have to go back into an area every five years. From an ecological point of view, that may not be much better, because our intervention in the system would be more frequent. I don't think we would ever want to go much past 20 years. Even that is a period 80 times longer than the quarterly report of a corporation.

"This is a difficult concept for companies to accept. After all, the people who are making the management decisions of a large corporation are usually not foresters or ecologists. They're economists, and are likely to think in terms of quarterly reports and shareholders.

"Of course, we've got to have these people, because if the companies go broke, then we wouldn't have a forest industry. But the problem I have with it is that they are the people who are driving the planning process. When you're planning the use of land you cannot afford to have the planning process based solely on economics; the planning has to be based on ecology.

"When management is based on ecology, we can bring in the economic advisors and ask, 'How do we fine-tune this from an economic point of view?' We can't have one without the other."

"You were talking about an area that's very much before the public now, the Stein Valley, not far west of here," I said. "It could be an ideal place to implement this sort of thinking."

"Look, it's going to be a beautiful day tomorrow, Joe. I think we should take a trip up into the Fountain Valley. It's a microcosm of the type of area we've been discussing, where there is the possibility of a completely integrated management plan. We can drive by the Stein Valley on our way back."

The morning was sunny as we set out for Fountain Valley, where his company was involved in land use planning. We drove across the bridge from Lillooet and north on Highway 12 until we came to an old road. This road was the original wagon road, and had been built by the natives and early gold-seekers. No agreement was ever made with the natives for this road right-of-way, yet it is used by all the local residents. The road passes right through the native village near the highway. Fountain village now has both power and water.

My guide explained, "In this particular valley we have the possibility of implementing a completely integrated management system. At this time, the Fountain Indian Band only has a say over what's happening on the actual reserve, not in the whole valley. Even then, in law at least, the authority isn't with the band, it's with the Crown, in other words the government. The band is simply a fabrication of the federal *Indian Act*. It has no power.

"At the present time, however, with their limited budget, they do hire planners. They got some money to do a physical development plan of the reserve itself. They hired me to work on land use planning in the entire valley, but ran out of funds. That's one of the things they're negotiating, more money. But some people get upset because they say the natives don't have any jurisdiction off their reserve. They only have jurisdiction over these little postage-stamp sized reserves. That's the reason they didn't get money to do more planning, because by implication it would recognize that they might have some further jurisdiction over the valley if they are allowed to do that sort of planning.

178

"I am merely the facilitator of the planning process," he continued. "The decisions are made by the native people who live and work there. As consultants, we look at the inventory and explain what's there. We also do all the graphics that help when you get to a band meeting, but the final decisions are theirs. I don't agree with some of their decisions. That's not the point. The point is they are going through the process of planning, of looking at the alternatives and deciding which are best for the land and the community.

"There is what's called a Coordinated Resource Management Plan for Fountain Valley. It was part of the so-called public participation process set up by the B.C. Ministry of Forests. It's a process I call *'repressive tolerance'*; that is, you allow people to come and complain and then you ignore what they say. The native people, really, have zero power in this system. The plan for that valley is still entirely in the hands of the Ministry of Forests and they do as they see fit.

"One spring I represented the band at one of these meetings. The chief was there. There was a lot of debate. That was before the road blockade, and the band was being cooperative. We really didn't want any logging going on in there until we'd got a sensible plan put together. However, we said okay because there was a five-year plan and maybe it was the beginning of a process where we could all cooperate. There'd been agreement in that five-year plan on an area that would be made available for small business sales. We were meeting every spring. Then we came back the next year and were informed by the B.C. Forest Service that they had just given a small business sale on a plot of land that wasn't even in that agreed-upon five-year plan.

"The chief just walked out. It's no wonder they don't want to be cooperative today. That's why it's so difficult to get a native chief to sit down and take part in the planning process, whether it's over the Stein or the Fountain Valley. Even when you have an agreed-upon planning process, the Forests Ministry won't use it.

"The native people feel that they're wasting their time. They want to set up their own process. This is why a lot of the blockades are happening. The natives are trying to force a meaningful negotiation process. The tactic may not work. It could end up backfiring and turning people against them. It's like the negotiations over the Duffey Lake Road."

In the summer of 1990, the native band at Pemberton, east of the ski resort of Whistler, claiming logging trucks were violating their land rights, blockaded for weeks the Pemberton to Lillooet road known as Duffey Lake Road. The blockade was page one and at the top of the six o'clock television news. Tempers flared between the natives and the residents of the village of Pemberton, the loggers and tourists. Arrests were made and charges laid but the dispute eventually simmered down.

"The natives still demand settlement of this land claim and the government insists the public and the loggers have the right to use the road. Nobody won this bitter dispute and nothing was accomplished to prevent a future confrontation.

"The Fountain Valley Road was the original wagon road and was built by the native people and those going to the gold rush. Then settlers came in and used it to get access to buy pieces of land. There is a quarter-section in the middle of the valley, which has a little postage stamp five-acre reserve in it. Years and years ago, when somebody preempted that 160 acres, the Indian people said, 'You can't give that piece of land to those people. We're using that land. We have a house on it and we're farming it'.

"So the Indian agent says, 'You're right. It can't be preempted if you're using it.'

"Then the agent and the settler go and measure how much land the Indian family is actually using, and exactly where their house and garden are located, and the agent takes that small area out of the block, makes it a reservation, and sells all the rest to the settler. Now, how can the native family expand their farm when the surrounding land is given to somebody else? Five acres per family was given for Indian reserves; a quarter-section per family was given for settlers. To this day, that five-acre postage stamp of a reserve is not an economic unit, and it can never be.

A look at a stand of virgin timber at higher elevations on the Duffey Lake Road between Lillooet and Pemberton, January 1991.

A reforested clearcut in the same general area showing five-year-old trees as they appear above two feet of snow.

"This past summer the owner decided to clearcut his 155 acres, but the Indian people have not accepted that the land is outside the jurisdiction of their reserve. So up went the roadblock, stopping any and all logs moving out of Fountain Valley. They were not going to allow those logs to leave the valley because the person who cut them didn't have that right. In the second place, they were hoping for an overall plan for the area, which would include all the people living there and using the land, whether they be native or not. But you don't hear that in the media."

When we were there, those controversial logs were still neatly stacked, ready for loading, and starting to decay. Only time will tell if they will be wasted, or if the band will allow them to be hauled away to a mill for processing.

We continued on down the narrow old road through this beautiful little valley, and eventually came back onto Highway 12. We then travelled south some 20 miles to where we could look across the Fraser River to the west and see the snowcapped Stein Mountains towering some 6,500 feet above the Stein River.

Dr. Chandler had been asked by the local natives to give his opinion on logging the Stein Valley, which the band considers to be their sacred ground. They have fished, camped and hunted there for centuries. He has hiked over the area many times.

As we sat looking at the spectacular scenery, I asked what his thoughts were on logging this valley. He was quick to reply, "I hope this valley will always be preserved in its natural state."

"Frankly," he said, "I'd rather see the Stein left out of any type of timber harvesting. From a land management point of view, the Stein is too valuable as a natural ecological laboratory to use it in any other way. As we begin to realize the mistakes we've made in land management, and as we try to restructure our management systems, we will need to refer to an area that we have not modified in any major way in order to find out how systems function naturally. The Stein is the perfect candidate for that role, because so many different ecological zones are represented in a relatively small area.

"Once the natives regain their say over the Stein Valley, it's quite likely that anyone who wanted to work in there could do so, provided they did so according to the plan approved by the natives. What I'd like to see is a planning board set up that is made up of native people, land use consultants, professional foresters, loggers and recreationists. The overall planning for the use of the area would be in the hands of the planning board. It would be responsible for setting cutting conditions and for actually supervising what, how much, and when it is cut. But I don't think the Stein Valley should ever be logged."

As we drove back towards Lillooet, Dr. Chandler pointed out some round pithouse foundations, some of which are reputed to be at least 7,000 years old. They could be seen mostly in the area northwest of where the Stein River flows into the Fraser. They were dug two to three feet into the ground to give protection from the cold winds blowing off the mountains. This was where the Indian bands spent the winter.

"The way the government deals with the Indians, Joe, is that the Forests Ministry comes to deal with them about forests, the Highways people come to deal with them about highway rights-of-way, the water rights people come and tell them how the water is to be used, the Crown Lands people allocate building lots, and the Mines Ministry issues mining or prospecting permits. It's a piecemeal way of looking at the land. The Indian mind sees it all as one thing. This valley is all one unit, and each of these components is just a part of the management of the whole valley. They would like to have all those issues negotiated as one. They're not opposed to coming to some sort of a settlement. They're not opposed to having non-Indians living and working in the Fountain Valley. What they want is a total management plan for the whole valley. They want to sit down and negotiate on all the issues together.

"In Canada today, we have a group of native leaders who are well educated in legal and financial issues. They're also in a position where, as a result of the devolution of the Department of Indian Affairs, the funds have been shifted over to the bands to use for what they consider to be the really important issues for their people, such as land for them to work on. The administrative structure of a lot of these band offices is really excellent. They occasionally have non-native consultants like myself at the administrative level when they realize they don't have a particular expertise among their own people. But I don't have any doubt that they have the ability to manage their land.

"Unfortunately, the attitude of many non-Indian people is that Indians don't know the rules of negotiating. They think that the first thing to do is make the Indians understand the white man's rules. That's a dangerous approach, because everybody knows how to negotiate in their own way. Different cultures negotiate in different ways. Generally, the native people can't respect the sort of labour/management negotiation which is really the only one that our society uses. The Indians use a consensus type of decision making process that takes much longer and which respects all of the minority views. The type of negotiating that our society generally uses ignores minorities.

"If you're in the group with less than 50 percent, you don't count. Both the natives and whites have to come to a common view of what negotiating is. Unfortunately, the arrogance of our society takes the attitude that other cultures have to learn how to do it our way. Until the process has been worked out, we can't possibly start arriving at a solution for land claim settlements.

"The biggest fear I have is that there won't be enough empathy towards working out a process. As a planner, my work is in process. A planner isn't somebody who dictates the way something should be done. It's somebody who tries to bring in all of the facts, the facts from nature, the facts from culture, and the facts from economics, and then have them all work together to arrive at an accepted outcome.

"There is often a great feeling of frustration on the part of the government people who sit down with Indian representatives. They tell the natives there will be a meeting on a certain day and then expect to reach immediate agreement. The native world simply doesn't work that way. They've been here 7,000 years or so and they're not going to be pressured. Sometimes it may appear they are very deliberately rejecting our culture, which puts those kinds of pressures on them. And they are. It is deliberate. They're stating that they don't want to be part of our world, and I think we have to respect that."

I asked, "Can you see a way where the Indians have their land and pay their taxes. Pay their way and be proud of who they are. Is that sort of expectation not possible?" I asked.

"That certainly is possible and it's clearly the agenda of the federal and provincial governments to head the negotiations in that direction. That's one of the reasons why, for instance, the Sechelt agreement is very important to the provincial government and why they brag about it as an example. The Sechelt Band now functions as a municipality and has all the powers of a municipality. The problem with that, of course, is that municipalities have no real power.

"Municipalities exist at the will of the provincial Legislature and, in fact, any by-laws that a municipality passes have to go to the Ministry of Municipal Affairs and be okayed. Otherwise it's not law. I don't see native bands agreeing to that level of intervention in their decision-making. They're talking about nationhood. Now 'nationhood' is a nebulous term, but it clearly means not having local decisions overseen by others. I don't think they are going to allow the same kind of looking over their shoulder that they get from the federal government. Most bands consider the Sechelt situation as a sellout.

"It's only in British Columbia and the north that we don't have agreements signed between the native bands and the federal government giving up title to the land. There are treaties all the way across Canada. Treaty Eight was the last one up in northern Alberta and in that corner of B.C. east of the Rockies. In all of the treaties, which were signed between the Indians and the federal government, or the Indians and the British Crown before that, the land was given up to settlers in exchange for education forever and no taxes. Those were deals made by treaties. That's the way we immigrants got possession of the land that makes Canada.

"But when we got to B.C., we didn't make any treaties, except for a bit of Vancouver Island where there were some signings under the auspices of the Hudson's Bay Company. No treaties have been signed anywhere else. So the original inhabitants are perfectly within their rights, according to British law, to consider that it's still all their land."

"In other words, the Indians can move into Vancouver and take it over?" I asked.

"One thing that's important to understand is that, as far as the native people are concerned, it's the provincial government that is claiming their land. We've got it backward when we say the Indians are claiming our land. The native people say they don't need a land claim, and they're making that very clear. They know it's their land; it's as simple as that. The Indians claim, 'It's you white people who are claiming our land. It's up to you to come and negotiate with us for the use that you want to make of our land.'"

"In effect then, no legal British Columbia title is worth the paper it's written on?" I suggested.

"It's important to understand the historical background," Dr. Chandler said. "The Indians are saying that the province's claim to hold title is illegal if you go back a long way to the Royal Proclamation of 1763. That Royal Proclamation basically said that no individual may make deals for land; deals had to be made on a nation-to-nation basis. Therefore, the British Crown must settle with the Indian bands for the land, and then the Crown can allocate the land to settlers. That's the theme of the Royal Proclamation."

"You're saying they didn't do that in British Columbia?" I asked.

"Yes. They didn't do that in British Columbia. By the time the settlers and everyone got here there was an arrogance that said, 'Well, we don't have to worry about that any more.' The fact that treaties were signed all the way across Canada indicates the intent of the Royal Proclamation. Again, it was all British law, but no proper treaties were ever done in British Columbia, so the situation becomes very complicated. In some cases, there were treaties signed under duress.

"In British history, if you lose a war and sign a treaty, that's considered a valid renunciation of title. Even that wasn't done here in B.C. We didn't say, 'We've got you guys cornered, now sign.' There wasn't any transfer of title. What it comes down to is that we have to sit down to some real negotiations with the native people.

"Even the position of the big companies now is to get it all settled. They really don't care if they pay their royalties to the provincial government or to a native government. I think the direction that things are going in British Columbia indicates that the forest companies will have less control. It's about time; they should never have been given the timber resources in the first place."

That was his flat and simple conclusion, one that could make every officer and director of every forest industry giant in B.C. reach for his bottle of aspirin—or the jug in his bottom desk drawer.

CHAPTER THIRTEEN

The Right Mix

Later, back at his home, Trevor Chandler continued with Lesson Two, based on his many years of dealing with forests, land and the men who manage or mismanage them and the Indians.

"When I was in East Africa, the concept of a forester was someone who was hired for one particular forest. It was a lifetime career. The forester would design and plan everything for that forest over his lifetime. He would literally get to know every tree."

"That's what they say about my friend Tom Wright," I said. "They say he's got a name for every tree on his woodlot. But even with all his tender loving care, he had a bad blowdown in one of his hemlock stands last winter. He considered it quite a loss. I told him to go in and log it, then replant."

"Well," said Chandler, "these kinds of things happen. Dealing with the unpredictability of a natural resource is all part of its complicated management. He may not have to replant because of natural regeneration. Mother Nature and hemlock work together well. If the soil retains all the organisms he will get a natural cycle of regeneration."

"There are quite a few opinions on burning. What do you think?" I asked.

"Well, I'll try to answer that as an ecologist. Forest ecology has been taught to most professional foresters. It's usually a little one semester course and is taught very selectively. They learn only the ecology that justifies the management methods they are using. That's a pretty strong statement for me to make I realize, but most foresters have been taught selective ecology.

"The history of forest ecology is that the first forest ecologists studied the recovery of forests from cataclysmic events, such as forest fires. Of course, nature has a process by which forests recover from cataclysmic events because they happen all the time. However, that is not quite the same as what happens in the natural evolution of a forest that is not affected by cataclysmic events. There are two different successional paths of the kind of change that is continually taking place in any ecosystem. One is the successional path that happens if you wipe out a forest and start again. The other is the successional path that is continually happening in any active ecosystem. There's a difference. Now, modern forestry is based on only looking at the response to cataclysmic events. They're saying, 'Okay, when we go and clearcut we're just doing the same thing as a fire does.'

"But when we use a system based on frequent cataclysms, or violent events, such as the grow, log, burn, grow, log, burn system we're currently using in B.C., when we go in and clearcut, we're not doing exactly the same thing a wild fire does. We're not creating a hot burn, and we're not leaving any standing wood or any large woody debris lying around. That's important. An old burn is a very different ecological situation from a clearcut. After a natural burn, there are still a lot of old trees and snags and brush, and the soil hasn't been as badly disturbed. Then the young trees come in and they get bigger and bigger. The snags fall and become the large woody debris on the ground. They release a lot of nutrients to the soil and hold in moisture. As the trees get bigger, the forest eventually reaches some kind of a steady-state situation where the old trees die and fall down and young trees are continually coming up under the canopy. That goes on and on forever, or till you have another fire that sets it back to zero.

"Along with the continually changing forest, there is a wide variety of other plants and animals that interact and evolve with that particular environment, such as the birds that eat the bugs. Cataclysmic events aren't all that frequent, even fires. But in general, I think we're getting more evidence that burning has a lot of negative features that we didn't realize.

"A managed forest, however, doesn't in any way try to imitate that natural cycle, at least not the way we manage forests today. We plant, let it grow for 70 or 100 years or whatever. Then we cut it and go right back to zero again. All of the other functions of a forest never manage to occur in that type of management system.

"We, as humans, have to take the approach of looking at a piece of land and identifying all its components. How do we optimize, make the best use of all those components? We shouldn't just say that we need to keep so many people working in the forest industry, therefore we need to keep cutting wood regardless.

"We then use an approach that we call integrated resource management by getting in some cattle or sheep, and putting up a few little campsites. But the primary use is still to take the trees out. We're still attempting to get the most we can out of the land, rather than optimize all its different components. That can't last. We'll not be able to sustain the land, let alone the forests, with that kind of approach. What will the oncoming generations be able to do with that land?

"In the long term, I think forestry is always going to be an important industry, but it's going to become less important as a proportion of our total economy for a number of reasons. There are other materials that we can use for building houses. Wood is nice, but it's going to become too expensive when all of the old timber is gone. It's going to be so much more expensive and so much more valuable that other building materials will be used."

I asked, "Do you promote small patches of clearcut?"

"No, small patches of clearcut don't necessarily work either. There are some areas where clearcutting makes sense. But in general, our first attempt should be to look at the way a forest naturally comes back, then go in and take out only a small percentage of the forest cover. I'm not saying that we should not do any clearcutting at all, but probably only a very small fraction of our logging should be done that way.

"Just think of a tree that's already 100 years old. Think in terms of the leaf area of that tree and the amount of sunlight it

Area and Volume Logged in B.C. 1911 to 1989

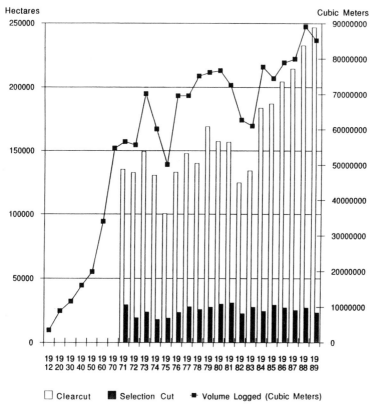

Graph showing the ratio of clearcutting to selective logging.

intercepts in relation to the amount of wood that will develop in one growth ring around that tree in one year. It's a lot of wood compared to what's added by a whole lot of little trees. The difference in volume of wood grown per acre is much higher if we do it with larger trees instead of with smaller ones.

"It's very basic. Not only that, we don't have the cost of putting in the seedlings. And natural regeneration takes place much better in a protected environment. As soon as we clearcut an area, we change the microclimate of that area dramatically; the conditions in that region are totally different. There are areas I can show you around here that were clearcut 10 or 15 years ago and there's not a tree growing there. Conditions are now beneficial for grasses. There's such a solid mat of grass that no tree can get established there. It's simply too dry once it's been opened up. As long as there was leaf coverage, there was enough moisture maintained in there, snowmelt was slowed down, there was some regeneration and the forest was doing fine."

"One example," I said, "is an area near Youbou on Vancouver Island, that was burnt by a slash fire that got away, and it has nothing growing in it 40 years later. This was the first fire that was put out by the big Mars waterbombers. I was there to watch the procedure from our camp boat out on the lake. That hillside was so hot and steep nothing else could get near the flames."

He nodded. "Even if we change the temperature by one degree in the spring, it can be enough to make the difference between whether it's going to regenerate or not; whether or not we can replant successfully, or whether they'd have to use a much more expensive replanting approach, such as putting in a little shade for each tree. It can be done. We can put little shade collars on each tree. There are a lot of ways that we can technologically overcome the damage we've done, but those solutions are expensive.

"Another part of the problem is the engineer's attitude towards forest management rather than the ecologist's. The ecologist's attitude is that you let nature do regeneration and you do management. You assist nature in doing that. The engineer's attitude is to take the trees off and then find a way to put the trees back. We invent these great machines that prepare the surface and all kinds of neat things to re-establish the forest. We're great at that, but the cost is horrendous, compared to taking the other approach. Over millions of years forests have evolved ways of re-establishing themselves. That's what we should be studying."

"Aren't they replanting in Sweden, Germany and those countries that have been practicing forestry for several hundred years?" I asked.

"Yes, they're replanting, and I think that a lot of their forest management is no more ecologically sound than ours. I think there are a lot of good things about it. But again, what's happening in areas like Germany is that where they're getting to second, third, sometimes even fourth cut rotation on replanted areas, the growth rates and yields have dropped way off because the nutrients aren't there. The land has been drained."

"Can the controlled chemical fertilizers they use sustain forest growth for the long term?" I asked.

"It's quite clear that the chemical fertilizer basis of agriculture isn't working that well. Why? Because we use soluble fertilizers, and a lot of the chemical leaches out and ends up in our lakes and rivers as pollutants. We sometimes end up triggering the wrong kind of growth, or the wrong species.

"Only the high quality sites, with deep soil on land that's reasonably flat and suitable to use equipment on, should be picked to do the German or Scandinavian type of intensive forestry. We can't do that on most of the sites in B.C. I think we're going to have to go right back to square one and look at the ecology of our system. Then we can decide how it can be harvested so that we don't have to go in and replant and fertilize on those poorer sites.

"There's nothing I'd like more than to be in the position of designing that sort of a system. The real absurdity is that Canada was one of the leaders in setting up the International Centre for Research in Agroforestry (ICRAF) based in Kenya. I was transferred from the International Development Research Centre to set up the basic research program in ICRAF's early days. Today it's a large centre and does a lot of very creative things, including developing new methods for deciding how to manage a piece of land.

They have developed a system called 'Diagnosis and Design.' The interesting thing is that the system is probably the most progressive system in the world for making management decisions for a piece of land in terms of all of its possibilities. To a great extent this project was funded by Canadian money. Canada is still a major supporter of ICRAF, and Canadian scientists are still involved in it, but we don't seem to use the information for our own land use problems.

"As I thumb through my *B.C. Ministry of Forests Land Management Handbook* and reflect on its cookbook approach to ecologically sound decision making, I can't help but wonder if Canada wouldn't benefit enormously from bringing back home the conceptual basis for agroforestry, the basic ideas behind it all. Perhaps our own Diagnosis and Design system would help us respect the ecological and social uniqueness of each bit of land, help us avoid land use confrontations and help us prevent our ever-expanding base of not-sufficiently-restocked (NSR) lands.

"In my view, one of the most important contributions of the focus on agroforestry has been its new way of looking at land-use systems. Agroforestry systems contain so many components. They are so location-specific, because they must be suited to cultural and economic requirements. They are neither agriculture nor forestry, and so they have been all but impossible to fit into our existing land evaluation systems.

"Agroforestry is emphatically not the practice of farming trees. It is a collective word for all land-use systems and practices in which woody perennials, or trees, are deliberately grown on the same land management unit as crops and/or animals. This can be either in some form of designated space or in a time sequence. To qualify as agroforestry, a given land-use system of practice must permit significant economic and ecological interactions between the woody and non-woody components. You've got to have the right mix.

"I had been involved for several years in worldwide research when I came back to Canada, but I found the Canadian people were not really interested in talking to me about forestry because I am not a Registered Professional Forester. A few years ago I was wondering whether I should take the course and become one. But I decided that I wouldn't. I don't believe that people's arms should be twisted into taking that blindered approach, that only-one-way approach, in order to be involved with the management of our Crown lands. I think what needs to change is the attitude that gives one profession so much power over the management of our Crown lands.

"I have proposed an agroforestry approach for the Stein Valley. If we want really good management systems, we're running out of forested areas that haven't already been interfered with. We have done so little forest ecology study in the past that we don't know how these systems function.

"There are a bunch of ecological reserves in B.C. They are so small that they don't function as a real forest. My feeling is that we have to choose an area, or two, where we have large areas of forest so that we don't have the edge effect on them. There we can study the interface between different ecological types, and have a study area where we can continually learn more and more about how that forest functions when we don't touch it.

"That's my vision of the greatest use of the Stein. The information we would get from an area like that of how a natural forest functions would be more valuable to the future of managed forestry than the amount of timber we could take out by any method today.

"I'm not against forestry. I want it to be possible for my son to be a forester if he wants to be. I want it to be possible for this community of Lillooet to live on as a forest community. But it won't be possible if we don't change our ways. It'll die. This village will die.

"Don't get the wrong idea. I'm not a radical conservationist. My background in Africa in agroforestry is exactly the opposite. It is in designing conservative systems that allow us to get the optimum production from a piece of land. The best use for everyone, the people and the government.

"In Africa, we were looking at systems that produced food as well as timber. That's why we call it agroforestry. As you know, people are starving over there. Naturally we wanted to have integrated management systems that produced both food and forest products from the same piece of land. We're not even thinking of studying that here in Canada. But on many of our marginal agricultural areas in this country we should be.

"Where I am asking for conservation, as an example, is in the Stein. We have to conserve some areas so that we will have the laboratory we need to understand more about how forests function naturally. Otherwise we're down the drain. Let the Stein Valley be a laboratory."

CHAPTER FOURTEEN

Decentralization at Work

Back on Vancouver Island, there is one community that demonstrates local government is more knowledgeable and concerned than Victoria or Ottawa, and that local people are far more efficient and productive than multinational corporations.

The Municipality of North Cowichan established a Forest Reserve on its vacant land by an act of Council in June 1946. This reserve consisted of 11,826 acres, from which the timber then was being sold to local loggers. But there was no reforestation of any kind being done until Graham Bruce was elected mayor in 1979. It came about when a friend, who lived in the area, came to his office and suggested that something should be done with the North Cowichan forests.

"What's there to do?" Graham asked. "The trees are growing aren't they?"

"Well, they're not in anywhere near the condition they should be in," was the reply. "There's a lot of money to be made if things are done right. You've got a great resource that is badly managed."

After an organized tour through the reserve, Greg Meredith, the local reporter for the *Victoria Times* wrote several provocative articles about intensive forestry. Local residents began showing interest. Don McMullan, then Chief Forester for B.C. Forest Products at their Crofton pulp mill got in touch with Graham. He recommended some planning should be started if they ever expected to have timber in the future—and the time to act was now!

Bruce and McMullan arranged a meeting, and the municipality's Forest Advisory Committee was formed with the original

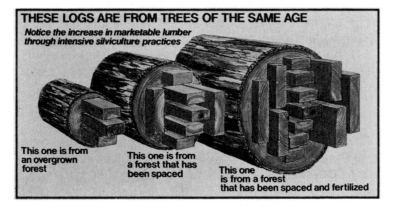

Pictures courtesy of the Municipality of North Cowichan and their Chief Forester, Darrell Frank.

members being: D. E. McMullan as chairman, and members K. N. Hart, S. Higginson, T. Walker, R. Elder and W. Schuckel. They met for the first time in the North Cowichan Municipal offices on March 27, 1981. Graham invited Gerry Burch, Vice-president of B.C. Forest Products to outline a good policy for the municipality to follow; a plan to get the project off on the right foot for the long march ahead.

Those volunteers put in hundreds of hours on mapping and doing inventories and reports, helped by local loggers and the business community. They produced a long-term plan for an intensively managed forest that would produce a sustainable yield and ensure their forest treasure would not be spent recklessly and wastefully.

The municipality, with the approval of the Forest Advisory Committee, hired T. M. Thomson & Associates Ltd. to do a complete timber resource inventory at a cost of $49,900. This included contour maps showing timbered areas and volumes, along with a working plan. Early in 1982, the committee hired Tom Haley, their first full-time Registered Professional Forester.

On May 7, 1982, a tree-planting ceremony took place on the grounds of the municipal hall just north of Duncan. Mayor Graham Bruce introduced Tom Waterland, the Provincial Minister of Forests who planted four tiny Douglas firs to commemorate the official start of the North Cowichan Intensive Forestry Management Program.

The 1981 recession was on. Dozens of families were on welfare. Graham remembers scores of people coming to his office looking for work which wasn't there. Times were tough. The municipality applied for available federal grants. A concerned official in Ottawa actually phoned North Cowichan stating they had substantial funds available if the unemployed in their area could be put to work in the new forest program.

Over the next four years more than 1,000 people planted, pruned, thinned and weeded the forests. Some of them had been teachers, secretaries, nurses, loggers, carpenters, and there was

199

even one marine biologist on the payroll—a broad cross-section of people who couldn't get work elsewhere during that period.

These workers soon developed a different opinion of what forestry was all about when it was supervised by professionals. They were proud to be doing something productive that would create security for the next generation. People who had been feeling pretty down about themselves, through no fault of their own, had now found meaningful employment. They soon realized their labour would eventually swell the coffers of the municipality and help keep taxes down.

In all, some $7 million has been received from the federal and provincial governments over the past 10 years to help make this "keep-our-forests-growing project" a reality. The following figures show the accomplishments and the jobs that were created as a result of this program.

Silviculture Accomplishments 1982-1990

ACTIVITY	HECTARES
Juvenile Spacing	1,923.7
Fertilization	1,511.0
Pruning	1,008.4
Site Preparation	350.3
Brushing and Weeding	912.7
Planting - 760,440 seedlings	869.4
Harvesting, Road rebuilding, etc.	630.8

EMPLOYMENT

Jobs Created	985
Number of Participants	1,586
Number of Weeks Worked	14,234

During 1991, approximately $450,000 was spent on the forest reserve on administration, road construction and their own fire-fighting crews and equipment. Of that amount, $350,000 would come directly from commercial log sales and $100,000 from a provincial government grant as a job creation investment.

In addition, North Cowichan has been able to build up a Reserve Fund of close to $500,000 plus interest. This "rainy day fund" will be used should there be an unexpected drop in log prices or a major fire.

At the time the forest renewal program was begun it was understood that all forestry management costs must be financed entirely through the cumulative revenues generated by sale of the timber or government grants. In the foreseeable future, the program will be able to more than pay its own way and contribute to the general revenue of the municipality.

The current forester, Darrell Frank, explains, "We're now logging the previously unmanaged stands where the volume of wood taken off varies considerably from area to area. The new managed stands will be more consistent, have a higher volume and be of higher value. Our annual sustainable cut is presently 23,000 cubic metres, but will double when the new stands are ready for harvesting, some within the next 10 years.

"We plan on doing only small area clearcutting," said Frank, "burning the slash in the spring, and replanting right away. Where it's not practical to do a total area burn, we'll go in and pile the slash and burn the piles, particulary in areas bordering on residential properties.

"The loggers are paid on a per cubic metre basis. They get the same price for all grades, whether they're pulp or saw logs. The municipality completed most of its first commercial thinning a couple of years ago when log prices were high, and it proved to be profitable.

"All our planning is based on an average 60-year cycle. Some of the better sites will have a shorter rotation while the poorer areas will take longer. We expect to double or triple our annual dollar return. With the province's ever-shrinking forest land base, we expect our crops are going to get more valuable each year.

"We are fortunate to have Doman's local sawmills and the big Fletcher Challenge pulp mill at Crofton, where there is always a ready and close market for our logs. Coastland Wood Industries Ltd. has a new plant in Nanaimo and they buy a good percentage of our smaller logs at even better prices. With their new process of making veneer, they can peel these small logs down to a 3.2-inch core.

"We also have access to a number of good logging contractors for our harvesting. Because of the mild climate, we are one of the first areas in the province to start planting in the spring. We are able to buy all our seedlings from local private nurseries that use seeds collected from the areas that are to be replanted.

"Last, but not by any means least, we're close and just to the west of the pleasant little city of Duncan, where people like to live and work.

"Eventually we hope to utilize the power line rights-of-way for growing Christmas trees. This year we also intend to experiment with sheep to help keep the brush and grass under control in our new plantations.

"The Forest Advisory Committee is composed of three public and three council members. It's a very practical group in that these people can be quickly contacted for advice. We can get several different outlooks and select the best to apply to our local needs.

"Our mayor, Rex Hollett, has carried on since Graham Bruce was elected Social Credit MLA for the Cowichan district. He has been with the program from the start and is still doing an excellent job."

Graham Bruce pointed out that, in contrast to the large provincial tree farm licenses, a municipal forest is usually situated close to a growing community.

"People whose yards back onto a timber reserve tend to look on these older forests as part of their own private park. However, logging them is not normally a problem when we explain that the older trees will be immediately replaced with healthy young seedlings. A healthy forest, especially a young one, cleans our air by taking in carbon dioxide and putting out oxygen. This is sometimes a pleasant surprise to the residents who had never considered this important aspect.

"Another part of public relations is to let people go in and cut firewood from the leftovers in a logging slash. The charge is $12.50 a cord, which just about covers the cost of the paper work. The local commercial price for a cord of wood ranges from $60 to $90 delivered.

"We also take groups of school children and outdoor clubs, such as Scouts and Guides, on tours through the woods to learn about an important part of their future, the growing young forest. Hiking, horseback riding, motorcycling, hunting and wildlife observation are other benefits enjoyed by both residents and tourists.

"When our pioneers first came to the west coast of Canada they burned hundreds of acres of perfectly good timber to clear the land so they could build their homes, grow crops and put in gardens. Trees in those days were considered a nuisance. There was never a thought that there might be a shortage. Now we've come to the point where we're starting to see the forests for what they really are: a renewable resource, an intrinsic part of our Canadian social fabric, both economically and environmentally.

"Logging is an exciting experience. When we take people from almost any part of the world up to see active logging and let them watch the massive machines handling huge logs like matchsticks, they never forget it, and they never seem to quit talking about it.

"Our North Cowichan experience has convinced me that things can be done on a smaller scale much more efficiently than the larger multinationals have been doing in our province," Graham observed. "That doesn't mean we shouldn't have larger components. At the manufacturing plant in Crofton, Fletcher Challenge is spending about $300 million in improvements. Most of that money will go directly toward improving the quality of the effluent that is discharged into our air and water. That takes a lot of capital. But I'm sure if you want a nice blend with all the other associated factors considered, most of the land should be privately managed. I believe North Cowichan is an excellent example of how that can be achieved.

"You're looking at between 50 to 80 years when it comes to growing a merchantable crop of timber. Investment in land management should only be made where there is some guarantee that the crops will be grown through to at least one full rotation.

"There are some very powerful forces operating when government starts dealing in our forests," Bruce cautioned. "Yes, certainly some of the larger operators seem to be putting heavy pressure on the powers-that-be when it comes to policy changes. Governments can change overnight and so can policies. That's why the Standing Committee on Forests and Lands, which I chair in the Legislature, is working almost day and night. We are now at a crossroad, where change must happen. Our committee must try to steer it in the best direction for all concerned. It's much too important to just let things drift. Setting of a policy that deals with all aspects of land use, not just logging, cannot be delayed.

"We have looked into establishing a Provincial Log Market. Such a market could certainly help eliminate the current protests from the public about exporting raw logs. We on the committee realize that the two things to be reviewed and dealt with right now are marketing and land use. This must be put in place at the earliest possible date if British Columbia is to continue being a substantial supplier of the world's pulp, paper and lumber products.

"In the last five years we've seen some pretty significant changes. For instance, passing legislation to deal with forests on private lands in British Columbia was unthinkable 10 years ago, though it is not unique. It's being done in the U.S.A. and many other countries around the world. We presently need a basic policy of intensive forestry guided by professional people with good common sense.

"I've lived in this community all my life, attended school and grew up with the people who live and work here. About five out of every eight people living in North Cowichan derive some part of their living from the forest, yet we rarely hear a word about forestry in our schools. Ten years ago, when I first became involved in our forestry program, I knew very little about logging or forests," Graham Bruce admitted.

"There certainly should be some place in our school system for teaching young students the basics of forestry. When I first started speaking at gatherings, all we had were forestry people talking to forestry people. It's no longer just the domain of the loggers and mill people. The general public has said, 'we want in. We want a say on environmental concerns, old-growth, wildlife, fish, clean water and recreation.'

"Clearly, there must be more opportunities for smaller operators and communities to have some form of land tenure. If smaller logging companies, local districts and municipalities are ever going to get into the growing and harvesting of trees, sustained yield and intensive forestry must be started at once.

"In the marketplace today, value-added products must be a priority if we are to maintain jobs and financial stability. In this community, there are a good number of small companies employing up to 30 people, doing special types of remanufacturing, producing innovative products, and doing it profitably. If that type of business is to grow, they must be able to get timber at reasonable, competitive prices. Today I would be hard-pressed to argue that our provincial forest policy is competitive, particularly when it comes to stumpage rates."

"Then you believe in a fair competitive system for procuring timber. The buying or selling by competitive auction," I suggested.

"Yes, I do. But it's like anything else, as we move ahead things are done that hadn't been considered possible only a year or two ago. We have to learn from the older countries. Here in B.C. we've already lost the best part of 40 years when it comes to growing trees on some of the large tree farm licences.

"I presented a paper called 'Strategy for Survival' to the 1986 National Forest Congress in Ottawa, on behalf of the mayors of

30 Vancouver Island communities. Based on our experience in North Cowichan, this report demonstrated how 300,000 jobs could be created throughout the country. At the same time it would halt the rapid demise of Canada's shrinking forests. In the process, it would certainly help to reduce the federal deficit by improving performance of the forest sector, the country's largest employer after government.

"Our research showed that an annual investment of $22.3 million will increase the value of the forest crop by $655 million annually; for every dollar put in, the improved value will be thirty-fold. Can there be any question as to the need for a national commitment to the future of Canada's forests.

"At the present time, we are getting piecemeal handouts from the two senior levels of government, not a long-term commitment of reinvestment. At the time the study was done, for every dollar received through forestry, the governments reinvested only seven cents. In fact, more money had been put into Canadair, the Ontario aircraft manufacturer, in the last eight years than into forestry. It was pointed out in this presentation that the forest industry is our bread and butter in British Columbia, and throughout Canada, for that matter. It is evident that unless a 'Strategy for Survival' is developed, the goose that lays the golden egg will soon look like a plucked crow!

"I've never worked in the woods, but I learn something new every time I walk through our forests. This industry is the most dynamic and interesting aspect of our province. It's the future of British Columbia. Properly managed, it can be with us forever.

CHAPTER FIFTEEN

Witherbee Tree Farm

It is becoming more and more apparent to me that smaller operators make the best job of reforestation and land use. And I personally believe that family-owned tree farms will guarantee the future of forestry. A case in point is the Witherby Tree Farm, owned and operated by Tom Wright and his son Bill.

Tom Wright was born in Warren, Pennsylvania, in 1916. He received his Bachelor of Science at Pennsylvania State University in 1937 and two years later his Master of Forestry at Duke University. He immediately joined the University of British Columbia where he taught Forest Economics, a fairly new subject in those days. From 1944 to 1946, he served in France and Belgium with the 796th Engineers Forestry Battalion of the U.S. Army.

After the war he returned to U.B.C., and in 1948 he was offered the job of Chief Forester at Canadian Forest Products (now Canfor) by Poldi Bentley, the owner and General Manager. While working for them, he served as the 14th president of the Association of British Columbia Professional Foresters.

In 1962, he again returned to U.B.C. as Dean of the Faculty of Forestry, with the blessing of the Bentleys. At the end of his two-year term as Dean, he returned as General Manager of all Canfor's coast logging, spending most of his working hours in and around the Nimpkish Valley. This area on northern Vancouver Island south of Port McNeill still has some of the finest old-growth Douglas fir and hemlock in the province.

"I'm really a bush rat, happy to be out there in November with the rain running down my face." So, after years of being behind a desk, Tom quit the corporate life. But he didn't leave the logging business, not by a long shot. Like many men who give up on office politics and corporate manners, he went consulting, working around the province, and even did a stint in Peru. Just to keep his mind nimble, he served as chairman of the Advisory Committee of the Small Business Projects, Vancouver Region, for the B.C. Forest Service.

"It was composed of six small loggers, and we handled projects and figured out the best way to help the people who applied for Crown timber. A good bunch of fellows," he said on the phone from his home in Vancouver where he is semi-retired.

He said he was one of the first private commercial foresters to work for the big logging companies, advising on forest reproduction and growth. Back in those days there was no thought of B.C. ever running out of timber, yet he saw it differently because of his experiences in Europe during the war.

He remembered the rumours in the timber business in the late 1940s. It was believed that H.R. MacMillan, the giant of the giants, did not have enough good timber for his sawmills. In 1950, Bill McMann, with whom Tom was working at Canfor, came into his office grinning from ear to ear, saying, "Tom, H.R. just solved his timber problems. He's amalgamated with the Bloedels." The big American-based operator had the timber but was short on mills, while MacMillan had mills but was short on timber.

The era of mergers and take-overs had begun.

Back in his days with Canfor, Tom found parcels of land on the Sechelt Peninsula, an hour's ferry ride from Horseshoe Bay, and decided he would be a small-time logger, tree farmer or woodlot operator, whatever term fitted.

His four properties eventually ranged from near the Port Mellon pulp mill on Howe Sound up the peninsula to Selma Park, and he is proud to say that his woodlot was the first licensed by the province in 1952 under legislation passed in 1951. "We call ourselves Canada's Smallest Logging Company," Tom said.

'We' is him and his son Bill, who quit the rat race with the Royal Bank of Canada and now runs the woodlot operation.

"With me looking over his shoulder," his father says. Some like to play golf, but you'll find us out in the woods, even on weekends."

In the summer of 1990, Tom invited Henry Castillou, one of his former students at U.B.C., and me to inspect his tree farm and woodlot near Sechelt.

Henry Castillou, of a well-known pioneering B.C. family in the Cariboo Country, graduated with a bachelor's degree, majoring in botany and forestry. He wrote his thesis on a tree disease known as 'root rot.'

He also earned his law degree, being admitted to the bar in the early 1950s. At that time, there were only four lawyers in B.C. who also held a degree in forestry.

At the Langdale terminal I met Tom and Henry coming off the early ferry from Horseshoe Bay. It was a warm sunny August morning and we piled into Tom Wright's 4-wheel drive and travelled north seven miles to his Witherby Tree Farm. We drove in about three-quarters of a mile east on a well-drained logging road he had built 30 years earlier.

Tom explained, "When I bought these 468 acres, there were only dirt and gravel roads anywhere on the Sunshine Coast, and the only real estate agent was an English fellow named Colridge. I asked him if he had any sizeable blocks of land with timber on them. After checking his records he produced a map and pointed to a block of land on the west shore of Howe Sound that had been preempted by a Mr. Witherby in 1892. It was then owned by his elderly daughter who lived in London."

Tom well remembers his excitement as he drove down that narrow road to the tiny village of Gibsons in the late '40s. He hired a fish boat and chugged north some 14 miles along the west shoreline of Howe Sound until they located the property by using the real estate agent's maps.

The fisherman stayed with his boat while Tom scrambled up the steep cliffs, often having to hang on to roots and shrubs to keep from sliding down. When he finally reached the plateau at the top he could hardly believe his eyes. This was exactly what he had been hoping for. After a brief rest, he walked on through the excellent second growth. There were a few veteran Douglas firs remaining from the oxen logging days of the early 1890s. The skid roads which had been built by hand labour over 60 years earlier could still be walked over.

Convinced he had found his dream, he hustled back to the realtor, made his offer and put down a deposit. Two months later the agent phoned, "Miss Witherby has accepted your offer."

"I'll bring you a cheque in the morning," was Tom's excited reply. He had a done deal, high hopes and great expectations.

Several weeks later, Miss Witherby wrote a very gracious letter and expressed her wish: "Mr. Wright, if you can ever use the name Witherby in connection with our property, I will be most grateful."

"This explains why the road is named Witherby Road and why the property is known as the Witherby Tree Farm. To our surprise, when we applied for the Tree Farm Licence in 1952, it was considered by the Department of Forestry to be the first small Tree Farm Licence issued up to that time."

We drove back onto the main road and travelled south for about one kilometre, turning west onto a steep logging road that took us up to the east part of his Woodlot Licence #10.

This Crown land was awarded the Wrights in 1984 to be managed in conjunction with his private holdings we had visited. The area is ideal timber-growing land with a minimum annual rainfall of 60 inches and up to 110. It is not unusual to get three inches of rain in a 24-hour period. This makes the area better for growing timber than for any other purpose, as the trees can prevent fast runoff and erosion.

It was a five-year-old mixed plantation of Douglas fir, hemlock and cedar. A winter wren had built her nest in one of the young firs and had laid a single egg. She flew out in a flutter of wings and chirpings.

"That proves wildlife can make a home in a young forest," Castillou observed.

Left to right: Joe Garner, Tom Wright and Henry Castillou, viewing the
nursery where Tom and his son grow their super-seedlings to a height of
five feet or more.

One of their super-seedlings planted in the spring of 1990. It was there a
winter wren had chosen to nest only months later.

Wright led us out into the slash and showed us how he was experimenting with some giant seedlings. "It's a phrase I guess we made up. A giant seedling is an older, bigger, tougher seedling. It can survive better." This area had been hand-planted earlier in the year and Tom was pleased with the way the whole sidehill was growing.

"Even with this year's exceptional drought," he explained, "it's gratifying to see how these five-year-old trees have survived and grown. We have been over this whole sidehill and replaced any trees that didn't survive. We had the option of spraying herbicides by helicopter or going in with axes and power saws to kill off the brush. Some of today's ecologists would like to see you in jail if you even suggest using herbicides, so we stayed with our axes."

Elaborating on his method of clearing brush to plant young trees, he said, "In this business, you should be trying things that are a little bit crazy. The brush, blackberries, everything, just grows so fast you wouldn't believe it. You can't expect a seedling to grow in there. They need sunlight and lots of it.

"So we go in with chain saws and axes and clean out the brush. We're talking about an area six by eight feet. That's hard work. I mean hard work. Then we plant our giant five-year-old seedlings.

"For a tree to survive, it has to kill off its neighbours. It's as simple as that. We help do that by cutting the brush. When you see the seedlings getting their heads above the brush, then they're away. It's exciting, two years later, to see these young trees with their three to four-foot leaders reaching for the sky."

There must be a lot of old timers around like me who think that Tom Wright is the most knowledgeable forester in the province, the man who would try anything to see if it worked.

As we drove higher up, he explained, "This stand of timber was originally logged with oxen and horses in 1902. For some reason, this particular area was never burned. As you can see, we have plenty of hemlock, which has recently developed a severe infection of mistletoe. This retards all growth and eventually kills the tree.

"Most people don't realize that fir only has a good seed crop every three or four years, while hemlock will seed every year. When you burn, the hemlock seeds are destroyed, and with natural regeneration, you can see that fir usually becomes the dominant species.

Discussing the pros and cons of slash burning, he reminisced, "When I was a director of the Pacific Logging Congress, I looked up the minutes of their first meeting held in 1914. They were debating the effects of slash burning and whether or not it should be continued. Apparently, there was no unanimous decision reached at that time and, to this day it remains a most controversial issue.

"Now we're coming into an area that was burned in 1904. It was mandatory in those days to burn every logging slash to eliminate the fire hazard. As a result, we've got a fir-hemlock mixture that is superior to any of our stands dominated by hemlock. As you know, fir is usually more wind-firm than hemlock and holds the stand together, preventing blow down. These trees are about 85 years old.

"The first commercial thinning was done with a portable spar. Then rubber-tired skidders or small cats were used to bring the logs out to the landings. Carl Gust did our thinning for years. He was a one-man outfit and had his own skidder. Another fine man," Tom said.

We now headed back to Langdale and on past Gibson's to Leek Road, where we turned into his next block of timber.

"Up on top where we clearcut small patches it's like a picture book," Wright said. "The new growth is now 13 years old and up to 25 feet in height. We used our giant seedlings to do most of the replanting."

As we drove further up the logging road, he pointed to a small clearcut and said, "We've just finished logging this two acres with our portable spar. We'll sell those two piles of alder and maple for firewood. There's a good market for it around here. We believe in cleaning up and utilizing everything. This wood will sell for about $90 a cord. But when we add up all the costs, including overhead and my son's wages, we'll be lucky to break even. We contract out everything. We've been very fortunate in having some good loggers work for us. A fellow named Bill MacDermott does most of our logging now. He took over when Carl Gust retired."

"How many acres do you have in total?" I asked Tom.

"The tree farm has 468 acres and the woodlot has 958. That's 1426 acres or, if you wish, 577 hectares."

"That's enough acreage to make a comfortable living for an average family," I suggested.

"When my son decided to join me on the tree farm I was delighted. He is now quite confident the change will prove to be a good one. When he was less than two years old, I would carry him to the tree farm in my pack-sack. When he got a bit older, he came with me every time he could."

"This is what I want to highlight, Tom. This is important: the security of a tree farm like yours that can be passed on from generation to generation," I said.

We drove to the other side of the property and he said, "We're now looking at what's left of our 32-year-old stand. This was our first clearcut. I needed some money to build roads so I had Mike Jackson log this small patch. This is how we get the capital to go on. This is the third crop of timber from the site. We have spaced this third stand and also cut out the alder and maple with power saws."

"You took out Japanese piling in here, didn't you?" Henry asked.

"That was our first thinning. Yes, we thinned out this stand for piling. Now we're presently taking out more piling with the logs. It works very well. Everything we do fits nicely.

"Intensive forestry is the new buzz word," Henry declared. "You're doing it. And doing it well."

"Well, you guys, here's an interesting fact. We practised this so-called intensive forestry in here and last winter we had some heavy wet snow and 20 percent of the remaining trees were flattened or badly broken. Yet we have a stand across the road that wasn't spaced and our losses were less than 2 percent. How about that? There's a lot we have to learn yet. There may be a lesson for us here. In some stands, maybe intensive forestry spacing practices are not worth a damn. The truth is, in the forestry profession most of us can't agree on anything. The present policy says you must space everything, that it's going to double the yield. I don't agree with that statement. A stand you were admiring up that road wasn't spaced, but it's putting on excellent growth rings.

"When you send a man in with a power saw to thin, he's instructed to cut down three trees out of every four. He can't really know which tree is growing in the best soil, or which one has the best chance of survival."

I suggested, "There should be an experienced professional forester on the site, putting a marker on the trees to be left standing."

We drove back to the highway, past Robert's Creek and turned onto Pell Road where there was another section of his woodlot.

"This area was planted early this spring and I've only seen a couple of dead trees. I feel sure that if these had not been our giant seedlings, the death rate would have been much greater.

"What we do is walk right into the brush, clear a small patch, plant a giant seedling and throw a bit of fertilizer in with it. As you know, once a fir can get to sunlight, no matter how much brush there is, the fir seedling will soon dominate. It will survive. It will grow. It will become a tree.

"We have our own nursery and support the position that everybody should be doing something a little bit different. Do something that's unusual. You have a 10 percent chance that something good will come of it, and in this case right here you can see it most certainly did.

"We grow our super seedlings in gallon pots. We use a combination of peat moss, topsoil, pearlite and sand. We also throw some long-lasting fertilizer in the bottom of every hole when we plant. My son Bill, who runs this now, figures he has about 5,000 pots. This is expensive so it can only be applied on the best growing sites. We're not big promoters of this. We just do it because we believe it will work. We find it can save time and money. We're doing this entirely at our own expense. We started this giant seedling project because the tree roots don't get damaged at all in the planting process."

"Those gallon pots are plastic, so I assume you can use them again and again," I said.

"Yes," Tom replied.

At the next site Tom said excitedly, "Look at this soil. This is the best you can get. It is a superb example of a good growing site because it is producing such heavy brush, yet the five-year-old fir are holding their own. It doesn't matter how much brush grows around them, those trees with their leaders up in the air, they'll make it and produce a fine stand of timber. This is the way to go. We're sure of that.

"I would say we have this area over 70 percent controlled, even though it looks like the devil with all the brush. Look at that hemlock. They're so interesting when they start out in such a flimsy-looking way. As you know, the more a hemlock droops over at the top, the faster it's growing. In spite of that, a hemlock usually grows straight as a ramrod."

"Don't you think you could get a grant from the government for this sort of experiment?" I asked.

"Maybe," he said.

"What is your tenure on this woodlot? What time element does the Forestry Service give you?"

"It's like a tree farm licence. We have a five-year renewable plan. This parcel here is about 300 acres."

"How do you pay your stumpage?" I asked.

"They charge us on a regular Forest Service appraisal. They price it like any other timber sale. They take under consideration the cost of building roads and other operating costs. Ollie Starvald, who died of cancer about six months ago, built our roads. He always said, 'There are three requirements for a good logging road—drainage, drainage and drainage.' We've had some good men working for us. I wish I could name them all.

"Our profit or loss depends, to a large extent, on the stumpage; how low, how high it is, and so far the Forest Service has been fair with us. That's why we try to do the best job possible."

"Do you consider this land to be more profitable to the province of British Columbia in timber, or would it be more profitable as a residential area?" I asked Tom, knowing his answer, and asking it really as a joke.

"Timber, timber, timber," he almost shouted.

"That's the answer," Henry laughed, and added, "I think there's plenty of space for housing down near the ocean. This rough terrain isn't currently needed for anything but the growing of trees."

Wright said, "Here at the bottom, for the sake of educational purposes, I have a walkway to where we cut off a stump at ground level so we could count the rings. Every ring means one year of growth. It was the largest fir on this 40-acre parcel. More than seven feet across. More than 900 years old. I wanted something to show the university students. We bring junior foresters out here and give them a bit of real history and education. Let them count back to when Columbus arrived.

"These young people, well, they're still in school and they've got a lot of ideas, but its big forestry they're talking about," Wright said. "They have certain ideas about this kind of operation. It makes for lively discussion I can tell you," and he laughed.

"To me, this is one of the most advanced experimental areas in British Columbia," I said.

"We're pretty small if you compare us with the big companies, but we know what we are doing," Wright said. "We were lucky to have this land awarded to us. As you probably know, if a person applies for a woodlot that is adjacent to their own private land that is being properly managed, the ministry considers that a plus. We have to regulate our operations on our tree farm in complete harmony with the woodlot. As a matter of fact, we submit our annual reports for both parcels jointly."

I said, "Your son has taken over from you. His son or daughter will probably take over from him, and so on. Your family can look forward to some long term security."

"Yes, Bill and his family are making a nice living, and it's a nice way of life," he said. "But there's plenty of hard work. Remember that. It's a marvelous objective. Whether it can be done in a practical and profitable way depends on the people themselves. I'm very much in favour of smaller private ownership of the land."

"If it's economical and has a future," I said, "you'll get the right people growing trees. You and your son are living proof of that, Tom."

The head office was a little wooden building with a big table and some benches. "This is where lunches are eaten and decisions are talked over and made," Tom said as we drank coffee and ate sandwiches and cookies. As so often happens, the talk drifted back to other times, probably pushed along because we had just seen a type of family reforestation and timber management which was completely alien to what we had experienced when we were in the business.

Henry recalled the days when he was my full partner in Samuel Island Logging Ltd., a company formed in 1956 to buy Samuel Island and log it. The 328-acre island is situated between Mayne and Saturna Islands and faces out onto the Gulf of Georgia; the lights of Vancouver could be seen on a clear night.

There was one large family home on the property and one three-room cottage where Henry lived with his wife and young family while we were logging. Our crew of 10 men slept and ate in the big house. Nearby was a well-built horse barn with a concrete floor and the very latest in steel pipe stalls, which became our temporary repair and welding shop. There was an excellent fresh-water spring and a good wharf and float where we could safely moor our camp boat.

We paid the princely sum of $48,000 for the island. After the logging was finished, we sold it through the same American real estate firm for $52,000.

The new owner built a landing strip adjacent to the big house. Shortly after, he was lost in a snowstorm flying between his American home and the island. This young man was married to the daughter of the famous U.S. aviator, Charles Lindbergh, who accomplished the first solo trans-Atlantic flight to Paris in 1927 in his single-engine aircraft. Lindbergh's daughter moved away after her husband's death.

"Don't you wish we'd kept Samuel Island, Joe?" Henry asked.

"Why do you ask?" I queried, but I was suspicious, knowing the price of waterfront property.

"Well, I just had it appraised last month by a realtor. Guess what? He came up with a market value of $13 million."

"Remember Henry, I suggested we keep it, but you didn't think you could afford it at the time," I said. "And I'm not sure I could have afforded it, either."

From where we sat we could look out the windows and see Christmas trees growing all along the B.C. Hydro power line.

"We soon discovered that Douglas fir make good Christmas trees," Wright explained. "They seed in naturally and we just prune and cut them, then haul them to market. We sell thousands each year. The ones that grow too tall for Christmas trees, we dig up and plant in our timber stands. Despite what many think, Christmas tree farming is not a profitable business. Even in the Fraser Valley, most of the Christmas tree growers I know are losing money because of the competition from Washington. The Americans seem to be able to bring trees across the line and sell them for less than it costs us to grow them."

Asked why they grew Christmas trees when there was no profit, he laughed and said, "Oh, we hope the time will come when we'll break even. Until then, growing them means we can put a few unemployed men to work for a couple of months each year."

After lunch we looked at another part of his woodlot, and our guide said, "Now we're on well-drained gravelly ground with plenty of rain and sunshine. I challenge anyone to grow anything more successfully here than Douglas fir."

"Those trees must be putting on more than four feet of height each year," I observed after measuring several of the young trees.

Wright replied, "I really believe the answer for growing a new forest is to get the land out of government hands and into private holdings where there's long-term security. You can't grow a forest on an assumption that you're going to get renewed tenure just by doing certain things," he said. "There's no long-term anything when the government can change overnight and set up a new policy. Let the people own the land or have a long-term lease with an option to renew."

We drove higher up the road and he stopped and said, "There's one stand left here that's 95 years old. When I made a study of the old-growth in the Nimpkish Valley, my conclusion about managing older stands was to thin them. We requested permission from the Ministry of Forests to thin this stand. We took out about 20 percent of the total volume. Here again, there is not much known about this type of management. We just had to use our own common sense, and it's paying off.

"We had a good logger in here with his rubber-tired skidder. He took out all the old and poorer trees. How do you like the look of it now that it's been thinned?"

"What's left standing is going to put on a lot of growth in a very short time," Henry observed.

"It's a dream logging show," I said. "Right on the road with a short yarding, and all on good flat land."

"In my opinion, some of the finest fir timber that ever grew started as a result of lightning fires," Wright said. "I made a map showing the ages of all the timber in the Nimpkish Valley. The finest stand was 385 years old and it produced one tree that was 305 feet tall. I personally checked to make sure I had the figures correct and sent them to the Forest Service. They said it was the tallest fir ever reported in British Columbia. The average total height of the fir in that stand was 278 feet, all with good tops, and the average diameter was 61 inches.

"There was also another area of 540-year-old timber, but most of those trees had lost their tops, so they would not grow any more and would start to decay. The 385-year-old stand had about 20 fir trees to the acre and the 540-year-old stand was down to 10. It just shows that in order to survive they have to kill off their neighbours," Wright pointed out again.

"When forest people read about this, let's hope it will be a boost for your type of tree farming," I said. "Good second-growth timber is the answer for all of the coast district, and I'd say for most of the Interior. Your whole operation is a model of what can be done. It has security and it is making money for your family. This project of yours is a perfect example of what is needed in most parts of British Columbia."

We reached the nursery where his son Bill was growing their seedlings. To get sufficient water, he had dammed a creek forming a circular pond shaded by alders. As well as giving them water for their nursery, it contained lots of rainbow trout which were constantly jumping, helping to keep the mosquito population down.

"Are any other nurseries using those larger containers for super seedlings?" I asked.

"No, we've been quiet about it. My son did have a call about them a few weeks ago from a forester at U.B.C. We run our own little operation and pay for our mistakes. Getting them up to the hillside is no easy task. It's just plain hard work.

"The big advantage of growing them in these larger pots is that they grow a much larger root mass," Wright explained. "It gives them a much better chance to survive. The one or two-year seedlings don't have that root strength."

"How many of those can you put into the back of a truck and deliver up to the planting site?"

He put up both hands, and with a big smile said, "Too damn many! Don't let anyone tell you this is an easy job. It isn't. We're on the go all the time. There's always something to be done. And you've got to be thinking all the time, and asking ourselves, 'What can we do to make it better?'.

"There's no easy way. There never will be," and he laughed and said, "But is it worth it? You bet it is. Some people love golf. I love trees."

There is no one in the forest business who will deny another due recognition for his achievements, but few actually receive something you can hold and say, "Here it is." Tom Wright is proud that four years ago the Association of B.C. Professional Foresters awarded him its Distinguished Forestry Award.

CHAPTER SIXTEEN

A Vision for Tomorrow

As longstanding members of the Truck Loggers Association and authors of books on logging, Curley Chittenden, Ian Mahood and I were alloted a display booth on the main floor of the Pan Pacific Hotel in January, 1991. There we met and talked with the general membership of the 48th Annual Truck Loggers Association meeting.

It was enjoyable chatting with the older loggers, but what I really wanted was some feedback on the Truck Loggers' submission to the newly formed Forest Resources Commission, "B.C. Forests—A Vision for Tomorrow."

The Truck Loggers Association was formed in the fall of 1943 at a meeting held in Vancouver. The small and independent logging companies believed they needed a strong organization to deal with the rumoured Forest Management Licences (which only the huge companies could qualify for) which could threaten their very existence.

Briefs from all sectors of the forest industry, including the Truck Loggers, had been submitted to the first Sloan Royal Commission on Forestry, which commenced on December 31, 1943. Sloan's recommendation for sustained yield as part of Forest Management Licences was handed down in December, 1945.

Forest Management Licence #1 was issued on May 4, 1948, for a huge timbered area covering both the Skeena River and Nass River watersheds by Forest and Lands Minister E.T. Kenney of the Liberal and Conservative coalition government.

This was the beginning of the end for many of the independent smaller sawmills and loggers. Many just sold their outfits and timber quotas to the bigger operators. They simply couldn't get any more timber at fair prices, so they either went contract logging, or out of the business.

To this day, the Truck Loggers Association (TLA) is still fighting to get more timber by reducing the size of the huge Tree Farm Licences. This could double the size of the Timber Supply Areas, the wood supply area for small operators, and could put more people working on sustainable forestry. This would give their present members some sense of security for the future.

The TLA made a submission to the Forest Resources Commission, which is investigating all aspects of the industry. The TLA Report was quick to point out a number of serious flaws in the industry's management approach:

For administrative purposes we have designated two types of silviculture—basic and intensive.

Basic silviculture is intended to reforest denuded land, and under regulations introduced in 1987, denuded land must be brought to a "free-to-grow" state. The flaw in this approach is that the requirement is only to establish a new forest that will reach a condition where it is able to grow on its own. This is not necessarily the same reforestation that would be done if the objective were to establish a stand of optimal volume, value and biological suitability.

The "free-to-grow" reforestation effort aims only at minimum standards. This ignores the physiological management of the new forest to the detriment of it's long term potential. It ignores more frequent silviculture which could enhance timber volumes and values in the stand.

A recent Forest Engineering Research in Canada report indicates that while the major licensees in 1985-87 spent $1.60 per cubic metre logged on forest renewal on their private lands, they spent only an average of .73 cents per cubic metre on Crown lands in settled and unsettled portions of the coast.

Comparable spending by forest companies in Washington in the same period ranged from 90 cents to $4.10, while in northern Europe $6 was spent for each cubic metre harvested!"

Another study at the University of British Columbia found that coastal TFL licensees (the major companies) spent $21.82 per productive hectare of their own money on the private portions of their lands, while only $5.40 per hectare of recoverable money, through stumpage offsets, was spent on the Crown lands they manage! These amounts included basic and intensive silvicultural treatments.

The only significant expenditures on incremental or intensive silviculture between 1985 and 1990 were the $56.4-million provided through the federal-provincial Forest Resource Development Agreement. This works out to an outlay of 20 cents per cubic metre of harvest, or 77 cents per productive hectare.

One of the consequences of the failure to establish a stable silviculture sector in the industry is that its labour pool is also unstable. There is a high rate of turnover, the educational and skill levels are low and there is little incentive for young people to contemplate a future in forestry management.

A recent report was quoted stating, "It was estimated by the Western Silvicultural Contractors' Association that during the 1989 season over 50 percent of the planters in the Prince George Region left in disgust at the poor wages and working conditions. The shortage of tree planters got so bad that some contractors were openly raiding each other's crews.

These are only some of the factors influencing the existing forest management situation. In B.C., forest research and development expenditures are 0.26 percent of sales. In the U.S. they are 1.5 percent, and in Sweden 1.75 percent.

When we should now be looking ahead to prosperity, we are faced instead with a declining resource, growing unemployment, falling real income levels, community destabilization and a disruption of the socio-economic structure of the province. In almost all areas the Annual Allowable Cut is fully or over-committed, and few opportunities exist for expansion or the creation of manufacturing plants to produce higher value products.

The Pearse Royal Commission recommended in its 1976 report that "the forest management policy for the future should be directed toward two related objectives: protection and enhancement of the capacity of forests to produce their potential range of industrial and environmental values; and within that framework the regulation of harvesting to produce the maximum long-term economic and social benefits from the forest."

His words were not heeded and we are now bearing the consequences—a declining timber supply and an aroused public.

Even though there are many differences between the Swedish and B.C. forests, they tend to cancel each other out. Sweden, being further north has a shorter growing season and less productive soils. It lacks our diversity in types of trees and the equivalent of our coastal rainforest. On the other hand, it has managed its forests for many decades, giving it a forest culture, a large, skilled work force and a sophisticated silvicultural infrastructure.

The following table compares the forest yields on the productive forest lands in Sweden and B.C. You don't have to be a mathematical genius to see that our forests need more attention.

TABLE I

	Forest Area	Annual Long Run Sustainable Yield	Annual Allowable Cut
Sweden	24 mill ha*	90 mill m3**	65 mill m3
B.C.	48 mill ha	72 mill m3	74 mill m3

* ha (hectare is 2.47 acres)
** m3 is about 1.31 cubic yards

One explanation for the much higher yields from the Swedish forests per hectare is that the utilization levels are much higher there. For example, pulp wood in Sweden is obtained from tops down to two inches in diameter, compared to four inches in B.C. The explanation for this difference in utilization is the existence in Sweden, and the absence here, of a working timber market in which prices are determined by supply and demand.

If loggers in B.C. could obtain market values for timber it would be economical to utilize much more of the wood now left in the slash.

The second factor is that the Swedish harvest is coming from stands that have been intensively managed for decades. Not only are the growth rates higher than ours, but the natural death that occurs during a growth cycle over the years is salvaged during thinning operations.

In B.C. the Truck Loggers' Association says it is "pursuing a forest policy whereby we are steadily increasing our annual cut, but extracting less value each year. Between 1961 and 1986, during which time the annual volume logged increased 242 percent, the value obtained from each cubic metre of wood logged declined 15 percent. What we have failed to do is sustain or increase the size of the work force by producing more valuable intermediate and final products."

After almost 45 years it is now evident that the forest department and the government of B.C. are not getting the results Gordon Sloan had envisioned. The following comparisons from other forest areas with proven forest policies show B.C. is in last place, not only in growing industrial forests, but also in manufacturing for added-value products and employing skilled people. The situation is disgraceful, as the following table illustrates:

TABLE II

	Value added/m3	Jobs/1000 m3
B.C.	$ 56.21	1.05
Other Canada	110.57	2.20
U.S.A.	173.81	3.55
New Zealand	170.88	5.00
Sweden	79.49	2.52

It should be pointed out that the $56.21 of added value in B.C. is based on the use of relatively high-value mature timber, while the $79.49 of value added in Sweden is accomplished by using lower value second and third growth forests.

In B.C. we are progressively getting less value from increased volumes of timber, and employing fewer people as time goes on. The expansion of pulp capacity on the coast, in combination with the growing control of timber tenures by the pulp companies, will only lead us further along the low-value, low-employment routes. Although under this strategy the profits may be high for the pulp companies, the provincial economy fails to realize a fair share as stumpage.

Also lost are revenues to the resource owner, the citizens of B.C. Between 1961 and 1986, the forest industry's share of the gross provincial product declined 32 percent. The value of forest product output has failed to keep pace with the rest of the provincial economy. The industrial strategy of high volume, low value commodity production in the pulp sector has been self-defeating. It has lowered the relative importance of the industry in the minds and lives of the people of B.C.

From 1982 to 1987 inclusive, it cost the British Columbia government $1.1-billion more to administer the forests than were received in forest sector revenues.

Further, because industry pays such a low price for its raw materials, there is a tendency not to value it. Hence, good sawlogs are often run through whole log chippers for pulp mill "feed," and logs which could produce veneer are turned into studs for construction.

Young stands that could be tended to provide a range of sawlog grades are designated as pulp forests that will be harvested at too young an age. In some cases we are cutting our most precious resource 30 years too soon!

Possibly the most significant difference between the B.C. forest industry and those in other countries with which we compete is the tenure system that determines access to and use of the forest resource. Comparing institutional characteristics of other forest nations demonstrates the peculiar tenure situation in Canada, and particularly in B.C.

TABLE III

	Forest area	Ownership Percentages			
	(mill ha)	Public	Corporate	Private	Other
Norway	7.5	18.0	-	75.0	6.0
Finland	22.0	23.6	7.4	65.3	3.7
Sweden	24.0	26.0	25.0	49.0	-
France	13.7	12.0	-	70.0	18.0
W.Germany	7.2	31.0	25.0	44.0	-
USSR	890.0	90.0	-	-	10.0
Japan	26.1	32.0	-	57.0	11.0
U.S.A	200.0	28.0	13.0	59.0	-
Canada	198	92.0	8.0	-	-
B.C.	48.0	94.0	5.0	1.0	-

In other advanced forest nations the normal tenure pattern is one of many owners of small parcels of forest land. In Sweden, for instance, the 49 percent of the forests privately owned are held in 240,000 parcels. In all of these countries a diverse pattern of forest owners and operators supply a log market that, in turn, supplies a diverse forest products industry. This includes major pulp and paper companies, which successfully compete in global markets with the limited number of competitive sellers that control most of the tenure in B.C.

When tenure arrangements in other nations are examined, along with the economic performance of their forest industries, it would appear that control of the forests by the mill owners is (as in the case of B.C.), in fact, an impediment to the growth of a diversified, world-class industry.

Because the Forest Management Licence tenure system introduced 45 years ago has failed, the B.C. forest industry is faced with a steadily declining timber supply. This supply cannot sustain the existing mills, which are producing commodities of declining value. Our choice at this time is to live with the consequences of a declining timber resource or make the necessary revisions in the Forest Management Licence system dominated completely by large Canadian and foreign-owned companies.

In B.C., there is a great deal of professional disagreement and little observation of biological responses to forest management practices. We have little experience in silviculture, and spend less than one cent on growth and yield research for every $100 spent on logging. It is, therefore, necessary to approach this subject carefully.

In 1984, Jack Walters, then director of the University of B.C. Research Forest, calculated that if we dedicated 13 million hectares of good and medium site forest land to timber, and implemented a full program of intensive management on it, it would be possible to produce 84 million cubic metres of industrial timber annually.

In 1984, the value of the 74.6 million cubic metres of timber cut in B.C. was the lowest of any comparable country.

TABLE IV

	Volume logged (mill m3)	Log value ($/m3)	Value-added ($/m3)	Jobs/ Mm3
B.C.	74.6	139.36	56.21	1.05
Other Canada	86.3	259.75	ll0.57	2.20
United States	410.3	430.85	173.81	3.55
New Zealand	5.3	577.22	170.88	5.0
Sweden	60.0	242.80	79.49	2.52

Much of the difference in log values can be explained by the distortions in timber values stemming from the tenure and appraisal systems used in B.C., particularly when we realize that some of the B.C. timber is valuable old-growth, and that other countries have less valuable new growth.

If, for instance, the total industry in B.C. was able to increase log value by an average of $100 per cubic metre, we would be adding $7.5-billion to the economic worth of a 1984-sized timber harvest. Clearly, this is an objective that could be realized only

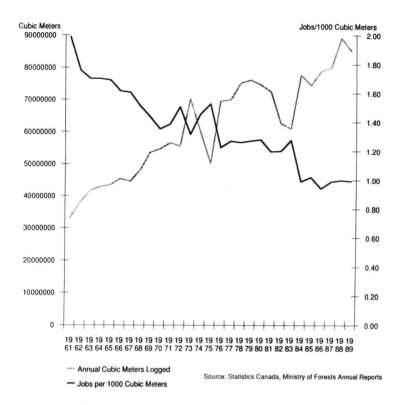

Graph showing ratio of direct forest industry related jobs to each thousand cubic metres logged from 1961 to 1989.

after several decades of effort, but it is a measure of the financial rewards available.

There are further opportunities to be realized from adding value in the manufacturing processes. As the value-added figures shown in Table IV indicate, in 1984 we averaged $56.21 in added value to each cubic metre of timber cut. If we could bring this up to even the Swedish level of $79.49, we could add almost $2-billion a year to our forest products sector. By a different measure of value, these activities would more than double the existing forest industry work force, with the potential of an additional 100,000 jobs in the woods and conversion plants.

The fact is, the forest lands of B.C. have a much higher productivity potential than those of Sweden. It is these lands that provide us with our competitive advantage in the long-term global forest products industry. The potential is there for B.C. to become the wealthiest forest products producer in the world.

First, we must manage our forests to get the highest possible industrial timber volumes and values while, at the same time, keeping as high as is possible the health and biological diversity of the forests.

Second, we must have more diversified forest tenure. The relatively uniform and concentrated institutions that have evolved over the past 50 years now need to be replaced with a larger number and broader scope of facilities in both the woods and our processing mills and plants. Our economic future depends on creating a diverse array of valuable products to sell around the world. This can best be accomplished by creating conditions that enable more new players to enter all phases of the industry.

Increasing the value of standing timber is the key to silviculture. In the same manner that increasing the value in a sawmill involves the fullest use of each log, increasing the value of a forest requires that the value of each tree be fully used. What is needed to accomplish this goal is a tenure system that puts skilled people to work in the forests to perform that task. The higher the value of the logs coming out of the forest, the higher will be the value of the products manufactured in the mills. What is required to obtain the highest values is an efficient means of timber distribution, between those who grow and harvest it and those who process it. The best way of doing this is through a free and open log market.

It is also important, vitally so, that timber prices be established in the market, and the manufacturing sector must pay the market price for timber. Only in this way can a fair and honest distribution of revenue occur so that funds are available for forest renewal that will sustain the industry in the future.

A paramount need is for the immediate implementation of a full forest inventory that will provide an accurate description of the province's forests, including an assessment of the state of the new forests. The success of any further changes in policy depends upon obtaining this inventory. How much forest has B.C. got? Nobody knows.

By managing the more productive working forest in a way that respects all forest values, the land-use conflicts now dividing the province can be avoided.

A primary requirement of any restructuring of provincial forest policy is the avoidance of quick change that would undermine and disrupt the economic welfare of individuals, families, communities and businesses. Although wide-ranging change is necessary, it must be undertaken using mechanisms and at a pace that allows for the orderly transition to a restructured forest sector.

It is necessary, then, to ensure that the timber supply of the existing mills and manufacturing plants is guaranteed at present levels until a functional market system of timber distribution is in place, and that if this volume is not provided, the company must be compensated for any financial loss. It is also necessary that this timber be available at a reasonable price and that the transition to market prices be phased-in over a period of say, five years.

The objective is to bring about major changes in the tenure system, the timber distribution system and the manufacturing sector so that the business and financial interests are not discouraged from maintaining investments in the province, that new employment is created without displacing existing workers, and that local economies are stabilized rather than threatened.

The fundamental weakness of the existing tenure system, dominated by a handful of big companies, is that it does not provide strong enough property rights to encourage these present FML holders to seriously engage in the business of intensive silviculture. Further, tenure rights have become concentrated to an extent that new entrants are excluded, that diversity has disappeared, and entrepreneurial activity is stifled. What is required is a reformed tenure system—a province-wide shake-up—that allows and encourages the development of a silvicultural capability which can increase timber yields and forest sustainability within the economic constraints of the marketplace.

One method of achieving this objective would be to transfer title to a portion of the Crown forests to the private sector so that the tenure structure in B.C. resembles more closely those which have evolved in other advanced forest nations. If this is not acceptable, what is required is a mechanism to assume the ultimate responsibility for the financial and managerial responsibility for a full, intensive silvicultural program. The Truck Loggers' Association's recommendations will concentrate on the second approach, and include certain key requirements:

A: Woods and manufacturing operations need to be separated by a timber market. This separation is required for several reasons. First, it will help insure that forest product revenues are distributed equitably between manufacturers, timber owners and producers so that the costs of renewing, tending and harvesting forests are available from forest incomes. Second, it will foster the creation of efficient forest management and harvesting practices. Third, it will make timber available to new conversion plants able to more competitively produce higher value products. And, fourth, it will accurately determine the market worth of the timber resource to insure that the public, which owns the resource, receives full value for its use. Therefore, we recommend that owners of conversion plants be prohibited from holding tenure on Crown land.

B: We propose that the entire designated working forest be allocated to licensees in the form of area-based tenures. This approach recognizes that the resource to be managed is the land, not just timber, and tenure agreements could include provision for the management of other resources in the management unit, eg. the development of hiking trails or a recreational fishery.

C: An upper limit needs to be placed on the size of the area-based tenures we propose. The reasons for this limit are, first, that economies of scale work against very large forest management and harvesting operations. Second, it is desirable, for the creation of a silviculturally intensive industry, to provide opportunities for as many management firms and as diverse a forest management community as possible. Therefore, we would recommend that the maximum size of management units be set at 200,000 hectares, which at present yields translates into an annual cut of 500,000 cubic metres. Allowable annual cuts on these management units would be increased or decreased according to the silvicultural performance of the tenure holder.

D: There needs to be a diverse range of tenure sizes to enable the participation in the industry of individuals, families, the existing logging and silvicultural contracting community and independent licensees, new companies created from present operational divisions of integrated licensees, Indian bands, municipalities and other local government bodies. The intention is to transform the existing logging and silvicultural industry, with additional entrants as indicated, into a diverse array of indigenous land-based tenure holders occupying the entire working forest.

E: The area-based tenures need to be renewable and saleable, and include a mechanism for the Crown to capture a fair portion of the capital gains realized upon disposal of the tenure. These features are required to facilitate the build-up of equity in the forest resources by the licensees.

The Truck Loggers believe that critical to the creation of a tenure system that retains public land ownership is an agency that assumes financial and managerial responsibility for the commercial forest. In order to attain financial and managerial autonomy, it needs to function at arm's length from government and the vicissitudes of the political process. A proposed Crown-led corporation would be created and, initially, 100 percent of its shares owned by the Crown. Let's call it "Forestco."

Capitalization of Forestco would be backed by the timber inventory. Shares would be issued to the public at appropriate intervals. Forestco would receive revenue from land rentals, stumpage on timber harvested and a share of the capital gains realized from licensees when tenures are sold. Forestco would guarantee the timber needs of the existing conversion plants at a reasonable price that, over five years, will be phased into the market price. It would also reimburse existing licensees for any improvements, such as roads and silvicultural expenditures, not previously covered by stumpage offsets or other means. Forestco would enter into long-term, replaceable area-based tenure agreements for the entire designated working forest.

They believe that if there was a mechanism for making land use decisions at the local level, not only would better decisions be made, but disagreements about land use planning could be resolved before they become divisive and insoluble. The people most concerned with sustaining the economic and ecological health of a given region are the people who live there.

It is the Truck Loggers' contention that real decision-making authority, as opposed to merely advisory mechanisms, must be decentralized. It does not seem necessary to create an additional level of government to deal with a matter as specific as land use planning. Give the regional district boards the necessary tools to perform the task of land-use decision making in their jurisdictions.

A resource revenue sharing formula should be created to retain within a regional district a portion of the public revenues generated by utilization of public resources. This share should be sufficient to cover the costs of administering the approval process, and could include amounts to provide for additional resource management functions.

And finally, the uncertainties created by the ongoing legal disputes over land claims is dividing communities, undermining business confidence and diverting the creative energies of many people. It is our recommendation that native land claims be resolved through negotiations, beginning immediately, and that the resolution include native participation in the mechanism of decentralized land use planning described above.

In conclusion, the Truck Loggers believe that underlying the debate concerning the future of the B.C. forest industry lies a profound and disturbing condition. We have lost, in this province, any sense of a common vision about our forests. *The owners of the forests, we, the citizens of B.C., have lost trust in the forest industry*. Every recent opinion poll indicates that British Columbians, like other Canadians, feel the forests are being poorly managed. These polls also show that most people blame industry for the problems.

As major players in the British Columbian coastal industry, we are as aware as anyone of the weaknesses in the way the forests are managed. But we are also aware of the origins of some of those weaknesses. But there is one deficiency that cannot be remedied by changes in the laws and regulations concerning use of the forests.

In Sweden, eight out of every ten people use or visit the forest every year. In most other countries where a working forest industry is based upon managed forests, there exists a widespread cultural attachment to forests. That degree of cultural connection to forests does not exist in British Columbia, although it may be growing. As a consequence, we suffer from a lack of understanding of both forest economy and human ecology. The future management of the forests requires the creation and growth of the cultural dimension at personal, community and provincial levels.

The control of the land is in the wrong hands, creating a powerful monopoly that can dictate to the government; a government which is already losing money and allowing the trees to be cut much faster than they are being grown. This must stop if the province expects to have a forest in the future.

That was the voice of the smaller loggers, the independents, the men and some women, who get out in the woods, use the chain saws, build the roads, fight the fires, and stand or fall on their own experience, ingenuity, determination and all-round savvy.

The Truck Loggers Association's submission to the Forest Resources Commission offers sensible, concrete points as seen from the perspective of the people who work in the forests. Issues like reforestation, value-added lumber, Tree Farm Licences, land use, timber markets, and the reduction of government and/or multinational power in the forest industry are discussed intelligently. The report's recommendations are a positive step toward a better future for British Columbians and their forests.

CHAPTER SEVENTEEN

The Way of the Future

Until the 1980s, most of the smaller second-growth timber on Vancouver Island was being cut and sold for firewood or left lying on the ground to rot when the stands were spaced.

Lumberman Don McKay came to Nanaimo on a holiday from the northern Interior of British Columbia, where he was extensively involved in handling smaller trees. While travelling around, he became concerned at this terrible waste. It seemed to him that only the bigger and best trees were being hauled out to be cut into lumber or chipped for pulp.

After some serious research, McKay concluded that Nanaimo Harbour was near the centre of one of the finest second-growth timber stands in the province. This 65 percent Douglas fir stand covers the east coast of Vancouver Island from the Malahat Mountains near Victoria up past Kelsey Bay, about 50 miles north of Campbell River. It includes the mainland coast and the islands from Bowen near Vancouver all the way to Minstrel, some 200 miles further north. This second and third-growth timber was growing much too thick in places and needed thinning, he concluded.

Don McKay's holiday resulted in one of the finest plywood veneer manufacturing plants in North America being built on the estuary of the Nanaimo River, on the west shore of Nanaimo Harbour.

Coastland Wood Industries Ltd., a state-of-the-art mill, began production on February 10, 1988, 10 months after the first bulldozer moved onto the site.

An opening ceremony was held on May 2nd, and McKay and his three partners invited Gerry Brown, the then-chief of the Nanaimo Indian Band to celebrate the new job-producing and total timber-utilization mill with a ceremonial prayer and blessing in true native fashion. The mill adjoins part of the band's 48-acre reserve within the city limits and this new company has leased several acres of Indian land for log storage. Coastland also has a verbal arrangement with the Band that reserve timber can be sold to the mill. And as part of their philosophy of community involvement, natives from the reserve, which had an 80 percent rate of unemployment, would be offered jobs.

The owners of the mill also invited politicians to the ceremony. First and foremost was Ted Schellenburg, the Progressive Conservative Member of Parliament for Nanaimo-Port Alberni, who had thrown his weight behind the project from day one. Others attending were Gerald Merrithew, federal Minister of State (Forestry and Mines) and Stan Hagen, provincial Minister of Advanced Education and Job Training. Also attending was Dave Parker, provincial Minister of Lands and Forests.

After the speeches, McKay had his crew start up the computerized lathe which ran off some 1/8 inch green fir veneer at 1,200 feet per minute with practically no noise—an impressive display. This raw veneer streamed down the nine-foot-wide conveyor at high speeds to be electronically trimmed and stacked for shipping. It was a sight never to be forgotten. Half an hour of technology working to perfection in a plant which not too long ago had been one man's vision and dream.

Financing the project proved interesting. The Bank of Nova Scotia was generous in their financial help to Coastland Wood Industries during construction and start-up, as were financiers from back east, who invested substantial pension funds in the project.

John Hesketh, whose business card reads "Vice-President, Manufacturing and Sales," said "Just call me plant boss." Choosing his words carefully: "To be honest, I don't think there was sufficient financing available for us anywhere in B.C."

In fairness, it should be said that even by 1987 not everyone was sure that B.C. had pulled out of the 1982 recession. It was only after the project was well under way that the federal and provincial governments jointly furnished a $3.6-million loan at 9 percent, fully repayable in five years. This quiet little non-polluting mill had already created over 50 new jobs in the mill itself, with a possible 100 more logging jobs in the district supplying logs and services.

In his bare bones office—two desks, four chairs and a filing cabinet—decorated with a two-foot yellow and black plastic parrot which somebody gave him because they felt Coastland needed a good luck mascot, Hesketh said, "Let's say the investors, other than the four partners, are like merchant bankers who, since ancient times, have been known as those willing to take risks."

Born in Saskatchewan 44 years ago but a native of B.C. since the age of six, Hesketh had 24 years in northern B.C. dealing with small mills and fighting for timber. When he joined Coastland in September of 1988, he and President McKay had worked out the company's philosophy. It was going to be a people-to-people and management-to-worker operation. "In fact," he said, "at our first meeting we really didn't talk much about the financial side of it. It was how we were going to get our workers involved and how we could all work together."

So, the mill is non-union, in a province and especially in an area where the industry is highly unionized. Hesketh said, "We had 1,300 applications for the 50 jobs for the two shifts we planned. They underwent aptitude tests and so on, because we were looking for the right people. They had to be intelligent, be willing to communicate with each other and be ambitious. We got applications from almost every province in Canada. We told ourselves, "With this new technology, unless we get the right people it will never be successful."

Of the 50 hired, 13 were local Indians and today nine remain; the one who would have been the 10th was killed in a recent auto accident.

Hesketh said, "When we got our workers together, we had a three-hour meeting and we said we'd like to be non-union. Everyone in this area told us it would never work. This was union country, strong union country. But we explained it to our workers. We asked for questions and we gave the answers. We explained that their pay would be about the same as the IWA rates, but their benefits, medical and such, would be above industry standards.

"Then we invited in the IWA organizer. He made his pitch, and the workers voted to be non-union. They are a good group of employees, and if they have problems, or if we have problems, we meet and talk it over. They know that anytime they want to join the IWA they can, but so far, they haven't.

"This is a small mill," Hesketh said. "We're little guys."

Little or not, when I drove onto the site there, were 11 big flat-deck trailers loaded with veneer waiting to be hooked to the tractors and hauled away to market. And the yard was stacked with logs. The boomboat in the offshore lease was pushing logs around ready to be lined up to enter the production process.

"We buy our logs on the open market. A developer can be clearing a couple of acres to build homes, and our log buyer will be there to bid for that timber. A farmer can have his land cleared for growing crops or grazing, and we'll be there to buy his logs. These are all second-growth trees, remember. He can deliver the logs himself or have them trucked to the mill yard," said Hesketh.

"We electronically scale the logs. If a trucker who has bought the logs from a farmer delivers on a Tuesday, we issue his cheque on Friday. This system works well for us and them. The independents don't have to wait for up to three weeks, as can happen when they deliver to other mills. We pay cash on delivery. Loggers like this. They are little guys, too, and often need that ready cash to pay wages and buy more timber. Doing it this way, we've built up loyalty."

If you have never been a gyppo logger and waited for as long as six months to get your money for logs delivered, you can't possibly imagine what this cash on delivery really means. It's like a bit of heaven, and contractors don't mind hauling extra miles to get it. It's a two-way street. The logger gets his money and the mill gets the logs it needs.

Hesketh said, "It also works in our favour at times when conditions are not good. This is an up-and-down industry. By paying right away we can often get some better deals.

"We buy from all over the country. I see our log buyer at our Monday morning staff meeting and then he's out on the road. We've even got guys hauling from as far away as Pemberton, which is a long, long haul to Squamish, where the logs are boomed and then towed to Nanaimo.

"We try to maintain a log inventory stacked in the yard or in booms of between two and three months. That makes us comfortable. We only ran short of logs once in three years and that was a combination of things—poor prices, too much snow, and so on. Our ability to use small commercial thinnings from lower elevations helps us get through the winters."

Another point is that if there is a strike in the logging, lumbering, or pulp and paper industry, non-union Coastland can continue to operate. No time is lost, no truckers on downtime. Hesketh estimates that in any year the revenue from the mill is above $20-million going directly into the local economy. But, when the three-for-one principle is applied, the value of the mill to the provincial economy is closer to $75 million.

"Not bad for a small outfit," he comments.

My first impression of Coastland's plywood veneer plant was it's clean, bright appearance, and the pride of the men working there. They all wore blue coveralls and blue hardhats, like the team they were. In an ordinary sawmill, you expect to see sawdust and other small litter on the floors, and wood dust on most of the machinery—not so here.

The rumble of the high speed machinery is not loud even inside the mill although in the past, and even now, some neighbours living up on the bluffs above the waterfront have complained. But the city council has backed the mill owners through these complaints and they, in turn, have alleviated noise pollution by limiting the periods at night when the big trucks can haul in or out of the site.

The shift foreman took me to where I could watch these small logs being processed through their state-of-the-art computerized lathe, specially designed to handle smaller second- and even third-growth timber as small as seven inches.

When these logs are sorted by species and size—the mill uses predominantly fir—they are then conveyed to the log processing deck where they are cut into exact 8.58-foot lengths. This is seven inches longer than the average sheet of plywood which, when trimmed, is eight feet by four feet. These logs are then put through the latest design of a Nicholson Murdie A5 35-inch debarker capable of handling 185 linear feet of logs per minute.

Now the most innovative part of the total manufacturing process: the debarked logs are put into conditioning chests. There are six of these long tanks where the logs are placed in hot water and soaked for 12 hours at a temperature of 140 degrees Fahrenheit. This water is recycled by using two big pumps capable of moving 960 gallons a minute. This fresh water is kept hot by two 8 million BTU Inproheat immersion heaters fueled by propane gas.

There are few air pollutants from propane fuel; there isn't even carbon buildup. By recycling the water, there is no pollution either. They plan on switching over to natural gas when it becomes available during the next few months. This will mean a 50 percent saving on heating costs.

It is this heat treatment on the veneer logs that is unique. The heat and the high tech drives on the ends of the logs make it possible to peel this small second-growth down to a 3.2-inch core. Using normal lathes, the cores are usually 5-1/2 inches or even more.

Now with a bit more fine-tuning, they believe these machines can peel the veneer off a log down to an astonishing two and a half inches. I asked, "Are you going into the walking cane business?" No, these cores can be sold to orchardists for propping up their fruit trees, or to vineyards to support the vines.

The bark from all logs is screened and sold as hog fuel to fire the boilers for nearby pulp mills. Any cull logs are put through the whole log chippers, screened to size and also sold to the pulp mills. The rest of the unsuitable waste material also goes in with the hog fuel for the pulp mills, including the smallest slivers, down to half an inch, which are automatically salvaged when the veneer is being trimmed. These small bits can be squeezed into high priced gluelam timbers, or made into pulp chips, depending on quality.

Even the bark that falls off in the yard or on the timber decks is gathered up and sold for mulch to be used in gardens. There is no burning necessary at this mill, therefore there is no smoke pollution or wasted wood.

In every truck load, there may be a few logs from the older dead-topped trees. These are usually rotten in the centre, making it impossible to keep the log spinning in the lathe. These cull-cores are stacked outside and transported to the small log chipper and made into pulp chips, making a profit where none existed before.

During their first year in operation their sales were over $20 million for some 300 million square feet of 1/8-inch veneer and the by-products. This was the result of two crews working two complete eight-hour shifts from 7 a.m. to 12 midnight. There would be 24 men on each shift, including the foremen.

McKay is one of the four shareholders, along with the eastern moneymen. There are no plans at present to take the company public and sell shares. If and when that day comes, their employees will have first refusal to buy at a special rate. A rise in the value of those shares will reward them handsomely.

Also a shareholder, Hesketh said, "Our first year we made money, our second year we lost, but it was in a bad market. This year we're not doing all that good, but when you look at the majors, losing millions and millions every quarter, we're doing okay. We're staying ahead. The lumber business is in hard times right now. Competition, tariffs, high taxes and a lot of other things. We're on schedule."

McKay believes production, quality and sales will all increase if they can get government to allot them a decent amount of timber, but so far Coastland has come up with a big fat zero.

While there is no confirmation, the word was that the government actually opposed the establishment of the mill because it felt there were too many in the area. So, there has been no movement towards giving Coastland a timber allotment to cut and haul on its own. Ironically, there is no other mill in the province that gets such excellent added-value for such poor quality logs.

Asked about the belief among many that plywood is finished, Hesketh snorted, "Plywood is not terminal." John showed me government sheets showing graphs that sales are just as high now as they were in 1985, despite the competition from waferboard and other new products.

He pointed out that their product is not plywood that you'd buy in sheets to make a shed. Their product is veneer, shaved from the log in one-eighth of an inch or less thick sheets, which are then used to make plywood or other products. In other words, the veneer is for re-manufacture into plywood or other wood products.

The trucks haul to manufacturing plants anywhere in B.C., Washington and Oregon, and large quantities are shipped to Japan. There is a plant on Annacis Island near New Westminster that takes the sheets and laminates them together with glue into beams which are rated stronger than steel.

"This is a very competitive market," says Hesketh. "There are many other plywood mills in B.C., but they have not reached the state-of-the-art technology that we have." Coastland is the only plywood veneer mill of its type on Vancouver Island and the most sophisticated of any in B.C. Coastland Wood Products is offering British Columbia something completely new.

"But so far," McKay said, "the B.C. Forest Service has not offered us one single tree. Yet we have been in operation for going on three years now. We are offering a $20 million manufacturing plant that can utilize all the commercial thinnings from millions and millions of acres of second-growth timber that belongs to the taxpayer. It is agreed that these young forests must be properly thinned if they are ever going to put on the growth they are capable of. I'm quite sure that every Registered Professional Forester in B.C. would agree that commercial thinning in our young forests is beneficial to both growth and value.

"Our Forests Ministry would be very foolish not to get the highest possible added-value for these thinnings. Veneer and gluelam beams are presently at the top of all lumber prices."

I questioned the economics by asking, "What is the difference between an eight-foot log averaging 10 inches in diameter sold as veneer and the value of the same log chipped and sold for pulp? After two minutes on the pocket computer, Hesketh said, "Well the veneer is worth 312 percent more than the chips." He clarified his calculations, "that's within half of one percent at today's prices."

"Here's how it is," he said. "This 10-inch log goes to a pulp mill as chips and eventually becomes a paper product. The value of that 10-inch log as chips is $3.978 to be precise. We are selling pulp chips every day.

"Now take that same log—when we've treated it in the hot water and run it through our lathes, the veneer we get from it is worth $11.126. Then, if we take what is left over from that same log and chip it and sell the chips we get an additional $1.60.

"Now, I'll do the arithmetic for you. Our mill chipping our own logs gets nearly four bucks. Producing veneer and selling the waste (waste is core and trimmings) as chips, we get a total of $12.732.

"On a percentage basis, Coastland gets 312.4 percent more value from a 10-inch log in veneer than in pulp chips."

I was astonished. It was more than I had ever expected, and especially in this day and age when there is so much comment in the media and by environmentalists about the condition of our forests and the need to make the most efficient use of them.

"Well, you don't have to be a genius to see that what you're doing must be the way of the future," I said.

Above: Sandy Maher, Angus McBean Nursery superintendent, and the author holding a Douglas fir super-seedling. In the wild this seedling would be one-third this size.

Right: One of the nurseries new and larger state-of-the-art glass-houses which can hold an average of 1 million seedlings. Douglas fir will start appearing after one week to ten days.

248

"Nanaimo Harbour is a wonderful location for our type of production." McKay continued, "We have a good highway at our back door and the Pacific Ocean at our front. We also have the CPR railway going through our mill property. We are located within 60 miles of 35 percent of all Canadian plywood production.

"Within that same 60 mile radius we are near half a dozen large pulp mills. There are deep-sea facilities less than two miles from the mill.

"This all makes truck shipping to the northwestern U.S.A. very practical. It seems we get more orders there than we can fill during the summer and early fall. Their prices not only cover the extra cost of trucking, but generally show some extra profit because of the exchange rate."

"In my opinion, all that is needed to make Coastland an even greater asset to the people of B.C. is land to grow trees on," I concluded. "And you also have one of the most advanced research tree nurseries in British Columbia right at your back door."

This seed orchard, at the Angus McBean Nursery on Yellow Point Road just south of Nanaimo, grows trees by grafting branches from superior trees. These branches are collected from various parts of the Island onto established root systems. MacMillan Bloedel have been the industrial leaders in research and reforestation since 1955. Picture courtesy of Erica McLeod.

CHAPTER EIGHTEEN

Has Anything Really Changed?

Multinationals are still squeezing the life out of our British Columbian entrepreneurs by cutting off their timber supply and getting away with it.

July of 1991 was the 30th anniversary of "Honest Bob's" release from jail after serving only two years and four months of his five-year sentence following the infamous 'Money Talks' bribery trial.

Since 1960, I have personally known at least two dozen substantial loggers, some with their own sawmills, who have been forced out of business because of the Tree Farm Licences. It seems our governments consider only the big operators with plenty of cash to be capable of handling Tree Farm Licences. So how much has it really changed?

Back in 1955, as allegations of bribery were being made and it had become obvious that the Forest Management Licence system recommended by the first Sloan Royal Commission in December of 1945 was not working, the second Royal Commission conducted by Chief Justice Gordon Sloan droned on. The Commission heard the ills and possible cures to British Columbia's system of forest land tenures, the Forest Management Licences (later called Tree Farm Licences) held by the major companies, and the demand by the smaller independent loggers for a fairer share of the publicly owned timber.

A man, broad of shoulder and heavy in the chest, rose to address the Commission. This was Harvey Reginald MacMillan. When he died in 1976 at the age of 91, 'H.R.' was front page news, just as he had been in life. In London, *The Times* wrote,

"More than any other man he is credited with establishing British Columbia as a major supplier of timber products to the world."

He had been appointed British Columbia's first Chief Forester in 1912 at the age of 26, and in 1916 he decided to find work in the timber industry.

On that day at the Sloan Commission, MacMillan could have sent one of his high powered vice-presidents, or one of its learned lawyers to enter a statement into the record. Instead, as the head of the company which controlled more privately owned timber and Tree Farm Licences than any other, he chose to make his own mark.

In his statement, he warned:

"It will be a sorry day for British Columbia when the forest industry here consists chiefly of a few big companies holding most of the timber...and all the better growing sites, to the disadvantage and early extermination of the most hard-working, virile, versatile and ingenious element of our population, the independent market logger....

"By 'independent market logger' we mean the logger who is free to make his own business decisions. He is an experienced man and has some capital, often mostly in the form of machinery. He is free to purchase timber, wherever he may find it, by government timber sales or elsewhere, or to seek logging contracts on privately owned timber. He decides how he will open up his show and the size of its operation. He makes his own choice as to whom he will buy from, sell to, join in contract with, or if he will operate as a contractor. If he borrows money, he chooses the lender, and he is not under duress in accepting the lender's terms. He owns his logs and does not have to agree to sell them below the market price as a usurious condition of getting a loan or being allowed the chance to go logging. If he makes a profit, it is his. If he makes a loss, he survives or goes into liquidation.

"There is every reason to avoid legislating or regulating his market out of existence. There is no apparent good or sufficient reason why any of the large companies should be aided by government policies to grow bigger at the expense of the smaller. Our forest industry is healthier if it consists of as many independents as can be supported."

The Sloan Commission droned on and the judge's report came out, but when all was said and done and the years rolled by, nothing really changed. The few big companies in the province today still hold more than 95 percent of the publicly owned forest through licences, and the independent loggers still scramble for timber or contracts to keep their operations alive.

On September 19, 1991, Sandy Peel, conducting the Forest Resources Commission study, capsulized his preliminary findings saying that the huge forest companies were still digging in their heels against the release of more of their timber to the independent loggers or woodlot operators. He predicted a loss of 120,000 jobs in the industry and related industries within the next 10 years.

Take the Sustut-Takla fiasco and the repercussions for little towns, such as Hazelton and Smithers. As Ken Bernsohn pointed out, their problems began back in 1988, when the government advertised it would be awarding a forest licence for a vast area known as the Sustut-Takla, 160 kilometers north of Hazelton and about 450 kilometers northwest of the nearest large city, Prince George. The licence would allow eight million cubic metres of wood to be removed from this never-logged area over a 20-year term.

A total of seven applications for all or part of the timber were received. Of those, key ones came from Westar Timber at Hazelton, West Fraser Mills at Smithers (the next nearest town) and two from Prince George—one a combined bid from Prince George Wood Preservers and Rustad Bros. Ltd., the other from Takla Track and Timber Ltd.

The applications were reviewed by a number of experts in the Forests Ministry, who came to the overwhelming conclusion that the best overall bids were from Westar and West Fraser Mills. In particular, they found the bids from those companies would provide more revenue to the government and would probably be in a better position to cope with market downturns than the Prince

George bids. The ministry was comfortable with the idea of building a road in from the Hazelton area rather than the Prince George idea of reviving or developing a railroad of more than double the distance.

The recommendations went to the Deputy Chief Forester, who was then the only person legally entitled to make the final decision. His recommendation was that all the wood go to Westar and West Fraser and none to Prince George. But he was prepared to consider splitting the cut (half to Hazelton-Smithers and half to Prince George) if the railway became a government priority.

The whole issue then went to Cabinet. After the Cabinet meeting, according to the Ombudsman's report, the Deputy Chief Forester was told Cabinet had decided all the wood should go to Prince George. The Deputy Chief Forester had no choice but to award the licence to the Prince George companies.

Also, according to the Ombudsman's report, Cabinet did not at that time have the power to make that decision or to *order* the Deputy Chief Forester to change his mind.

The Hazelton council says the impact of the decision has been appalling on that small community. More than 300 forestry jobs have been lost since then. The mill has shut down and is now for sale.

"The predominantly native communities of the Upper Skeena regions have been forced to cope with destabilization and disbelief as relatively wealthy Prince George has, by its voting power, grabbed resources which it has no logical right to receive," wrote Deputy Mayor Eric Janze.

"The human toll in abuse, crime and cynicism are apparent in our region every day. It is as if a part of our future has been ripped from the hands of our children."

In July, 1991, the Village of Hazelton took the whole matter to the B.C. Supreme Court for a judicial hearing. Hazelton wanted the Cabinet's decision overturned, the forest licence application reopened, and damages for the loss of the licence.

On September 18, 1991, one month before a provincial general election, I phoned Hazelton's Town Hall. I was told they had recently been in court for one full day. The outcome? A postponement of the hearing for six months!

Only the previous week, *The Vancouver Sun* disclosed an internal report signed by the Forests Ministry's two top officials stating that the Ministry is falling "so far behind" in calculating how many trees should be cut each year that it has "lost its leadership in the field of timber analysis." The 43-page internal report signed by Chief Forester John Cuthbert and Assistant Deputy Minister of Operations Wes Cheston was considered so formidable that the Minister of Forests, Claude Richmond, immediately ordered a freeze on cutting levels across B.C.

Industry spokesmen said this report only confirms what has been known for years; that the B.C. Forests Ministry does not have the data it needs to make informed decisions on the harvesting of our forests.

Industry observers said one of their concerns was that the province's forest inventory could be over-valued by as much as 20 percent.

Jim Pine, an environmentalist and one-time forest industry scaler, said the same conclusions now being drawn by the ministry about losses due to soil erosion were known five years ago. A report funded by the federal and provincial governments then concluded that future losses due to soil erosion in logged areas could total $80 million a year.

Closer monitoring of the logging practices of the major companies and increasing the number of woodlots can surely be part of the answer. Ownership, whether private or by stewardship through a government licence, requires a great deal of knowledge, some of it common sense through experience and some adhering to a large number of B.C. Forest Service rules and regulations.

One must consider that a woodlot will long outlive this generation and these skills of management must be passed on from one generation to the next.

Woodlotting in B.C. at present can in no way be compared to the forest giants who have Tree Farm Licences. Nevertheless, while only 1 percent of the forest land is in private hands, it does represent more than 2.5 million acres owned or leased by some 21,000 operators, with properties ranging from 50 to 5,000 acres. This represents 21,000 families earning part or all of their living from their woodlots. In Sweden, which has a population of 8 million compared to B.C.'s 3.2 million, there are 250,000 private landowners doing the same thing on slightly less than half the acreage we have here.

David Smith, president of the South Island Woodlot Association said, "Although small in area, these properties comprise some of the most productive forest land in B.C., and interest in their management is growing..." Organization among B.C.'s woodlot operators is not nearly as extensive as in Sweden or other European countries.

In his 1945 report on forestry stemming from his first Royal Commission, Chief Justice Sloan did recognize the value of woodlots and recommended that interested families be allowed 640 acres (one square mile) for their use as small forest operations.

This never happened.

While this small scale intensive 'farming' of the forest could sustain, in part, many more families and small manufacturing plants, it should be noted that 94 percent of B.C.'s vast provincial forests are controlled by the government and 86 percent of that is now in the hands of a few major companies. Therefore, the emphasis is on large scale logging and the overseeing of it by the understaffed B.C. Forest Service. This leaves precious little time to deal with the small operator, even though his role in the forest economy has been recognized as being beneficial to the province's economy.

The fact remains that the annual cut from these 21,000 woodlot operators is only one half of one percent of the log production of the forest giants.

The number of applications for small holdings far exceeds the number of forested parcels of land being put up by the Forest Service, so it is evident that individuals, many of them present or former loggers, realize the value of woodlot forestry. These indi-

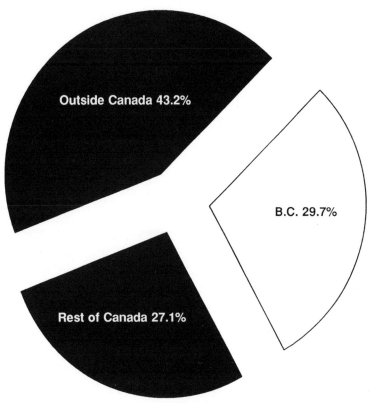

Outside Canada 43.2%

B.C. 29.7%

Rest of Canada 27.1%

Source: Deloitte & Touche (B.C. Central Credit Union)

Control of B.C. forest companies by location of majority shareholders, 1990. Source: Deloitte & Touche (B.C. Central Credit Union)

viduals are willing to take on these 15-year leases and operate them as businesses for the good of themselves, their families, their community and the province itself. However, the slow and uneven movement of the Forest Service bureaucracy has slowed the process almost to a stop. This is frustrating to many, and suspicious to others. This must be changed! Surely it's time government listened to and heeded the Forest Resources Commission recommendations made to it.

However, let us not overlook the aspect of recycling old newspapers and other similar material to eliminate, in part, the need for using so many trees to keep up with the demand for pulp.

Dr. Michael Davis, Vice-president of Development and Corporate Research for the Jefferson Smurfit Corporation and their Container Corporation, of America has his headquarters just outside Chicago, Illinois. He has been involved in this type of research for over 20 years, especially with the removal of ink from newsprint and its disposal. They find that the best method of getting rid of this sludgy black substance is to spray it over hog fuel, leave it out in the sun to dry and then burn it in their steam boilers.

These two companies operate 19 pulp mills in the U.S.A., using a high percentage of recycled fibre to obtain the quality and quantities of pulp materials they need. At times the disposal companies are actually paying for the privilege of leaving off their paper garbage at the mills.

Smurfits have over a million acres of land in Florida and Georgia, where they harvest trees on an 18-year rotation. Because of the hot and humid climate, these trees need little or no attention other than minor trimming and thinning.

They also have plantations in Venezuela, which mature in eight to nine years and require no attention whatsoever. The seedlings are planted where they want the trees to grow and the survival rate is virtually 100 percent.

Jefferson Smurfit Corporation is one of the largest pulp manufacturing consortiums in the world, if not the largest. It's head office is in Dublin, Ireland.

If we expect to survive on the world market with this type of competition, we had better take a leaf out of their book and learn to recycle as well as grow trees.

Now, in September 1991, the population of British Columbia is slightly over 3.2 million. It is projected that sometime early in the next century our population will have more than doubled. It follows that based on Sweden's example we could use ten times the number of woodlots we have today, creating thousands of necessary jobs growing trees on these smaller holdings. This would be intensive forestry and sustained yield.

A question we should be asking ourselves is: "Are our forests being managed for the benefit of the forest or for the benefit of the forest industry?" Let us hope the powers that be will heed the warnings H.R. MacMillan gave us in 1955.

It seems obvious to me that as long as control of our forest land remains in the hands of politicians, honesty, fairness, sound judgment and the future of our province will continue to take a back seat to power and greed.

Tomorrow is another day.

Logging Glossary

A-Frame: Giant A-frame structure on a big log float, which supports blocks and running lines in high-lead logging, used to swing logs from the back spar to the water or yard directly into the water.

Allowable Annual Cut (AAC): The volume of timber which may be cut on an annual basis from a given area of land.

Anchor Stump: Ground anchor for guy lines, skyline or tail holds.

Arch: Steel arch used to raise the front end of logs up off the ground for easier yarding.

Asparagus: Smaller logs bundled and strapped together for better loading and transportation.

Backcut: Cut put in the tree opposite the undercut.

Backfire: A fire purposely set to burn a fire break. Gas or diesel engines firing too soon backfires.

Backline: That portion of the haulback between spar tree and tail block.

Back Rigger: The man that rigs the back spars.

Back Spar: Spar tree at the back end of a skyline.

Bag Boom: Boom sticks coupled together to encircle and contain loose logs.

Barber Chair: When a tree splits leaving a slab attached to the stump resembling a chair back.

Barge: A type of scow for transportating logs or machinery.

Beads: Chokers, knobs etc.

Bean Burner: A poor camp cook.

Bell: Closed choker hook.

Benson Raft: A system of getting logs through rough water. Used before barges.

BFM: Board foot measure.

Bicycle: Carriage that travels on a skyline to prevent hangups.

Bight: A dangerous place—inside the angle of a fouled line.

Bindle: The roll of blankets carried by a transient logger.

Bird Dog: To point out. A smaller plane used to guide waterbombers over forest fires to where water is most needed.

Block: Steel sheaves to prevent line wear; added pulling power.

Board Hole: The notch cut in a tree for a spring-board.

Boom: Logs stowed and swiftered.

Boomerang: Spark arrester to reverse sparks down into a screen so they don't drift out to start fires.

Boomman or Boomcat: A man handy with a pike pole, catty on his feet and knows how to sort and stow logs.

Boomstick: A 66-foot log bored at each end, usually with a four-inch auger. Uniform in size with a minimum top size of 10 inches.

Broad-axe: A heavy axe with a very wide blade and short offset handle.

Brow Log: Log used to protect log cars or trucks while loading at a landing. Also used at logdumps to protect piling and hold rail cars or trucks in place.

Bucker: A skilled worker who saws felled trees into lengths.

Buckle Guys: Cables fastened tight part way up the spar to keep it steady.

Buckskin: Log with no bark.

Bull Block: The big block near the top of a spar tree that carries the main line.

Bull Bucker: The boss of the falling and bucking crews.

Bull Car: Big flat rail car used to move heavy equipment.

Bullchoker: Extra strong and long choker used on heavy pulls.

Bullcook: Usually a broken down old logger who takes little or no sass from the crew. Keeps the camp clean and gets in the wood.

Bulldozer: A track machine used to build roads, yard logs and do any one of a hundred other jobs.

Bull Hook: Large hook on the end of the drum line of a cat or bulldozer.

Bull of the Woods: Superintendent or woods boss. This term sometimes related to high riggers or other toughies.

Bull Pen: Where logs are dumped and held in the water for sorting.

Bull Skinner: Today a legend of yore. A man that knew how to cuss well and handle oxen from a single yoke up to a dozen. Sometimes known as bull whackers or bull punchers.

Bull Team: Used in early logging before horses came into use on the skid roads.

Bunch it: Quit.

Bundle-boom: A boom of bundled logs. Bundles are held together with wire cables or steel bundling straps.

Bunk: That part of a logging car or truck where logs rest when being hauled. A bed of sorts where loggers slept.

Bunk-bound: The condition that exists when logs loaded on a rail car extend far enough to interfere with logs on the next car and bind up on curves. Logging trucks became bunk-bound on sharp curves before compensating bars, or sliding reaches were used.

Bunk Load: The first layer of logs loaded onto a railway car or a logging truck.

Bunk Scales: Scale that came into use about 1950 to weigh logs on the truck. Public highways were limited to load weights with heavy fines for overloads.

Butt Rigging: Hooks and swivelled connections to the main line haulback and chokers.

Camp-tender: A boat that brought in the crews and cookhouse supplies. Also did odd jobs around a booming ground or take an injured logger to hospital.

Cant: A log partly or wholly square-cut.

Catterpillar/Cat: A track machine used for logging.

Cat Doctor: A mechanic who specializes in track equipment and capable of swinging a 10 lb. sledge.

Cat Skinner: Tractor operator.

Cat Side: Good ground where cats are used to bring logs to the landing or into the water.

Caulk: Steel nails driven into the soles of logging boots.

Chaser: Man who unhooks chokers at the spar.

Cayuse: A maverick—captured wild horse that doesn't like work or being ridden.

Cheese Block: Wedge shaped steel block to hold the logs in place on the bunks of the skeleton cars or logging trucks.

Cherry Picker: A machine for picking up lost logs or loading along a right-of-way where short yarding is feasible.

Choker: A bell and two knobs on a short length of wire rope to go around a log, then attached to the butt rigging and main line. Cat chokers usually have a bell and knob with an eye splice for the open bullhook.

Chokerhole: Is sometimes necessary to dig or poke a hole under a log in order to get a choker around it.

Chokerman: One who hooks chokers around the logs to be yarded.

Chuck/Saltchuck: The sea or ocean.

Chunk: In high-lead operations using a wooden spar and a McLean boom—the short log hanging from a block fixed to a buckle guy which acts as a counter-weight when the boom is swung. See slack puller.

Claim: Timbered country staked for logging.

Clear: Knot-free log or lumber.

Clearcut: Complete removal of all trees over an area at one time.

Cold Deck: A pile of logs left for future loading or yarding. Usually taken in on a skyline.

Coldshut: An unwelded link joint—like a shackle with no screw pin but with a riveted closure (can be riveted without heat).

Conky: Unsound timber infested with a parasite fungus growth.

Cord: 128 cubic feet of loose wood which equals a stack eight feet long, four feet high and four feet wide, split or round. Such a pile is usually calculated to contain 100 cubic feet of solid wood.

Core: Centre of a cable—can be a steel or hemp rope. The centre of a log that is left after being peeled for plywood.

Crib: Stack of telephone poles that floats in the water ready for transport. Some pole cribs were 50' long, 30' wide and up to 20' deep and lashed at the corners. Logs, timbers or boulders used as a retaining wall.

Cross-haul: Now a legend, it was an intersection of two skidroads going in different directions where oxen or horses pulled logs.

Crown Fire: Forest fire that spreads through the tree tops and travels like the wind.

Cruiser: A skilled woodsman who can estimate the quantity and quality of standing timber.

Crummy: A vehicle for transporting logging crews to work.

Cull: Logs or lumber of no merchantable value.

Cunit: 100 cubic feet of wood.

Deadhead: Partly submerged log.

Donkey Engine: Named because of its noisy puffing, snorting and loud whistles. A steam pot, gasoline or diesel engine with drums and cables that yards the logs from woods.

Donkey Puncher: A man who operates a donkey.

Dozer Boat: A powerful little boom boat with unique steering.

Duplex: A large skidder that both yards and loads logs.

Eyesplice: A loop spliced into the end of a cable or rope.

Fair Lead: An arrangement of rollers or sheaves on the front end of the donkey sleighs to guide the lines so they spooled properly on the drums. Also used on the heel boom on the shovel loaders or on top of the steel spars or towers.

Fake: Usually a gas donkey that was a bit haywire.

Fall: To cut down or fell trees.

Fall block: A long block used on skyline shows to give better lift for the turn as it heads for the landing.

Faller: A worker who cuts down trees.

Farmer: One who logs part time and lives on a stump ranch. Sometimes called a home-guard.

Fingerlink: A steel link that can be released under strain.

Firebreak: Any road or clearing that can help stop a fire.

Flat Boom: Usually eight sections, 66' wide and 540' long, of sorted logs stowed and swiftered ready for towing. Generally used for inside waters.

Flowery Holt: Something unusual being tried to clear a hangup.

Flume: Used extensively to carry shingle bolts down from the sidehills into a lake or river. Rarely used for logs in western Canada.

Flunkey/Flunky: One who helps in the cookhouse. A waitress, dish washer or both, depending on the number of loggers.

Flying-choker: A choker with the open hook cut down so that it will free itself from the log when tension is released.

Fore-and-aft: Road of logs laid end to end so the old roading donkeys could slide bigger loads down to the saltchuck.

Gandy-dancer: Railroad section worker.

Gilcrest Jack: Extensively used by hand-loggers to roll or push logs toward the chuck.

Gin Pole: Short leaning spar used for loading or unloading logs.

Goat: Small donkey usually used by the bull gang for rigging spars.

Grade Shovel: A large mechanical scoop shovel usually mounted on tracks and used in road building.

Grapple: Large powerful, mechanical tongs used to pick up or yard logs.

Grapple Carriage: A carriage designed to carry a grapple out from a landing making use of a tail-holt and haulback.

Grapple Yarder: Machine which yards logs using a grapple. Now being used by helicopters.

Grapple Yarding: New concept of removing logs by the use of a grapple, eliminating the need for chokermen.

Ground Lead: Old style of logging before there were spar trees. The logs were dragged on the ground.

Guthammer: Was a triangular piece of metal hung on a wire outside the cookhouse door. The cook would bang this with an iron bar to announce mealtimes.

Guy Line: A cable stretched between a stump and the top of a spar tree or tower to keep them in a solid upright position.

Gyppo: To log on contract. Used for any logging show that is fairly small and haywire.

Gypsy: Upright steam yarding spool. One of the first steam yarding units to go into the British Columbia woods used this type near Chemainus.

Hand Faller/Hand Feller: Logger who cuts trees down using an axe and crosscut saw.

Hand-logger: A man working by himself. Gilcrest jacks, axe, peavey, swede fiddles and a good rowboat were standard equipment.

Hangup: A log fouled up in a root, snag or stump.

Haulback: Line attached to the main line which returns the butt rigging and chokers back to woods.

Hay Burner: An ox or horse used for logging.

Haywire Show: Logging operation with poor equipment and rough ground—sometimes has no money for pay days.

Headloader: Almost another legend. Person who picks out the logs to be loaded and directs the loading of railway cars or trucks.

Heel Boom: A slanting, tapered boom (sometimes on a converted power shovel) attached directly to a machine used for loading logs. One end of the log rests against the boom while in the grip of a grapple or tongs suspended from the end of the boom, giving the engineer leverage and control to swing logs onto a truck or rail car.

Highball: Descriptive of any logging operation where speed is king.

High Lead: To yard logs to the landing using a spar tree to lift the log ends so that they don't hang up so often.

High Lead Block: See Bull block.

High Rigger/Rigger: The man who tops and prepares a spar tree for logging and is usually in charge of the side.

Hindu: The cable coupling or link between the strawline and the haulback.

266

Hogan's Alley: Walkway between bunkhouses and washhouse. A tough and dangerous street in Vancouver.

Hog: Locomotive pulling logging cars.

Hog Fuel: Bark and other wood waste, normally used to fire steam boilers for heat or power.

Hogger: Locomotive engineer.

Homeguard: A logger who is content to remain working for one company instead of moving about from camp to camp. Can also mean a farmer logger.

Hooker/Hooktender: The boss of the yarding crew.

Holt: The application of a special hitch.

Hot Deck: Is when the logs are taken away as soon as they land at the spar.

Hot Logging: When most turns are loaded immediately or logs are taken from a yarder as they come in—no pile is allowed to accumulate.

Inkslinger: A timekeeper, or office man.

Jackpot: A hell of a mess. A jumble of crisscrossed logs in a bullpen, usually where the logs are dumped into the water. A log jam on a river drive.

Jagger: A steel strand from a worn or damaged cable.

Jam: Logs or debris blocking a river.

Jewelry: The rigging designed for attaching logs to the mainline. Includes buttrigging, shackles, hooks and chokers etc.

Jill Poke: A strong pole or timber rigged to push logs off a rail car or log truck.

Landing: An area where logs are assembled for loading or dumped into the water.

Leverman: Loading engineer—especially the engineer who operates a donkey used in loading.

Line-horse: A legend used to haul the line back into the timber before haulback cables and two drum yarders were invented.

Loading Boom: Any of variously shaped extensions jutting out from a loading machine or a spar tree to provide a means for lifting of logs onto trucks or railway cars.

267

Loading Jack: A block suspended on a guyline for loading.

Locie/Loci/Lokey: A steam locomotive used on railroads.

Long-butt: A defective portion of a felled tree usually cut off and left at the stump.

Long Splice: Two cables of the same size unstranded then wrapped (or woven) together, then neatly tucked to form a continuous cable of close to the original size.

Lookout: Tower on high ground used in the summer to watch for fires.

m3: Cubic metre.

Man-cather: An employment agent whose job it was to induce holidaying loggers to get back on the job.

Marlinspike: A sharp-ended, tapered steel tool for splicing cable.

MFBM: A much-used abreviation for 1000-board-measure of lumber or logs.

Mm3: A thousand cubic metres.

Mobile Spar/Portable Spar: These portable steel spars are mounted on sleighs, wheels or tracks. This was the beginning of the end of the need for the high-riggers and the conventional wooden spars.

Molly Hogan: A link made of a single cable strand to connect cables or keep shackle and block pins in place.

Mug-up: Coffee and a sandwich, or either, usually between meals.

Mulligan Mixer: Camp cook.

Muzzle Loader: Bunks side-by-side where men crawled in over the end. A gun loaded with a ramrod before breach loaders were invented.

Nose Bag Show: A setting where a lunch bucket is necessary.

Nose-guy: The line that holds the front end of a Heel or McLean type boom suspended from the spar tree.

Nut Splitter: Mechanic.

Outrigger: The hydraulic legs which support the corners of a mobile spar, grapple loader or other machines.

Parbuckle: A way to roll or load logs on ships or trucks using two lines. Very heavy or extra long logs can be put aboard safely.

Passline: The line by which a highrigger moves up and down the tree once the tree is topped. Also moves heavy blocks and cables into position. Usually 3/8" or 1/2" inch cable.

Patch Logging: A system of leaving trees for a seed source or firebreak and clearcutting the areas in between.

Peak Log: The top log on any load, also known as a peaker.

Peavey: Lumberjack cant-hook with spike on the end; used to roll logs. Sometimes called a log wrench.

Peeler: A highgrade log suitable for making plywood or veneer.

Pig: A narrow sled formerly used on the old skidroads to carry tools and buckets of skid grease.

Pile or Piling: A small log driven vertically into lake or ocean bottom, usually to support a wharf. Piling is also used to form boom packets and other log or ship tieups such as dolphins.

Powder Monkey: A person trained to use dynamite with a valid blasting certificate.

Pre-load: To make ready a complete load of logs for trucks by using a spare trailer or log cradle to save loading time.

Prelog: To take out the windfalls and smaller trees before logging the main crop of big trees.

Pull the Pin: To quit your job, get your pay and leave camp.

Punk/Whistle punk: A person who gives the signals from the rigging crew to the machine operator either by hand, a jerk-wire, or an electric-operated whistle.

Push: A woods boss or superintendent.

Quota: A given amount of timber allotted to a sawmill or logger.

Radio Talkie-tooter: Takes the place of a whistle punk. (See punk.)

Ranchers: Greenhorns or unskilled loggers.

Reach: The steel tubing that connects the logging trailer to the truck. In earlier years a square timber or a stout peeled pole was used.

Receding Line: A line which takes the carriage back into the woods on a skyline.

Rider: A swifter or boomstick pulled across to keep logs from jumping over the head or tail stick of a flat boom. Usually about 14 feet in from both ends of the boom.

Rigging Slinger: The man who picks out the logs for the next turn, gives the signals and helps fight hangups. Second in command to the hooker.

Roll: To rob a man while he is drunk or under the influence of narcotics.

Rub-tree: A tree left standing in a high-lead setting and used to guide the rigging around some obstacle.

Salvage Logging: Logging done to clean up the small logs, chunks and miscellaneous pieces that remain after high-lead yarding. Originally this timber was left to rot or be burned.

Sawbones: A doctor or first aid person.

Saw Log: Larger logs suitable for lumber manufacturing.

Scabline: The haulback line between the tail block and the spar which has a block hung on it to give additional lift to the logs being yarded.

Schoolmarm: A log or tree which forks into two tops. Loggers describe it as a log that won't roll over.

Scissor Bill: A dull or stupid person.

Second-Growth: Trees that are planted or naturally reseeded and come up after an area is logged and or burned.

Second Loader: A tongman who works with and under the head-loader.

Section: A portion of a flat boom equal to the length of one boomstick (66 feet). Also section of road or rail line.

Setting: A logging side with timber within reach for yarding by one spar tree and yarding donkey.

Shay: Gear-driven locomotive.

Shear Log/Shear Timber: Timber or log used to unload logs into the water or onto the landing by pushing them sideways.

Shovel Loader: A grade shovel converted to a log loader.

Shovel Operator: A person who operates any grade shovel, grapple loader or heel boom system attached to shovel systems.

Show: A logging operation of any size.

Side Push: A strawboss, or one who bosses one complete side.

Side-stick: The boomsticks on each side of the flat booms.

Sidewinder: A sapling knocked sideways by another tree or bull-dozer or a yarded log. Very dangerous.

Silviculture: The science and art of growing and tending forest crops.

Skeleton Car: A railroad log car with just the two bunks and timbers connecting the two sets of wheels together.

Skidder: Machine for pulling logs on a skyline at high speeds or a cat and arch hauling logs to the water or landing.

Skidroad: A legend. Roadway with cross logs half buried in the ground over which logs were dragged from the bush using horses or oxen. This type of logging ended around the turn of the century.

Sky-hook: A logger's dream for tough yarding. Recently that dream has become reality with the use of helicopters.

Skyline: A heavy cable stretching between two spaces for aerial yarding.

Slack Skyline: A logging method using a skyline that can be mechanically slackened off by the engineer then tightened up again to make easier yarding. Such a system enables the sky-line to be pulled to the side and thus covers a considerable amount of the setting without changing roads.

Slack-puller: A chunk of log hung on the line and heavy enough to pull slack.

Slash: Any logged off area. To cut down trees. To slash a line through bush for surveying, or slash a road allowance.

Slash Fire: A fire or fires that are set to burn the residue of a logged over area. Usually lighted by ground crews or with a helicopter using fire balls.

Snag: A standing dead tree. A fire hazard that should be felled.

Snatch Block: Block which can be opened on one side only.

Snipe: Bevelling of log ends to aid in skidding over skid roads. On donkey sleigh runners to make moving easier.

Sniper: The man who does the sniping, usually with a sharp axe and/or powersaw.

Snoose: Copenhagen snuff chewed by loggers instead of tobacco or smoking cigarettes.

Snooser: A Scandinavian logger.

Snorkel: Wooden extension to a logging boom. Used for both loading and short yarding.

Snubbing Machine: Usually a big single-drum machine with a heavy line used to hold any load from runnning away on steep downhill grades. Usually has water-cooled brakes.

Spar Tree: Tree topped and limbed for use in high lead or skyline logging.

Speeder: Another legend that used to carry men by rail out to and from the woods. Same as a crummy, but only on a railroad show.

Spotting Line: A cable used to spot and hold rail cars for loading.

Springboard: A board shod with iron on one end so it can hold in a tree. The old timers stood on these boards to cut down the big trees.

Square Lead: Yarding at right angles to the spar tree. Not recommended.

Stag: To cut off logger pants somewhere between knee and ankle.

Stake: The amount of money a logger takes to town for his holiday. Upright steel posts at each end of the log bunks to hold the load in a correct and safe position.

Standing Boom: Double boomsticks fastened and floating at the entrance to the different sorting pockets. Boomsticks that surround the bull pen or other permanent holding enclosure.

Stemwinder: A geared locomotive; a Shay.

Stow: To put logs end to end in a flat boom before swiftering. Also stow logs or cargo on a ship.

Strawline: A light wire cable used to pull the haulback out through the tail blocks, also to change roads and rigging.

Stumpage: The price paid for standing timber.

Stumper: A tree that slides directly into the water when it is cut down and leaves its stump. A handlogger's term.

Suicide Show: A steep sidehill operation that's dangerous.

272

Sustained Yield: Harvesting only as much timber as the land can reproduce in say 50 to 70 years.

Swamp Hook: A hook used to roll a log up out of the mud so it can be properly choked and yarded. An L-shaped hook.

Swede Fiddle: A falling or bucking saw pulled by hand.

Swifter: A smaller boomstick pulled across a stowed flat boom and chained at both ends connecting it to the side sticks. This holds the boom straight and tight.

Tagline: A cable to control a grapple.

Tail Block: A haulback block strapped to a stump, so that the haulback cable can pull the mainline, butt rigging and chokers back to hook up the next turn.

Tail-holt: The back fastening for the haulback or skyline. Usually a large stump.

Tail-stick: The boomstick across the back end of a flat boom.

Talkie-tooter: A small transistorized transmitter which can blow whistle signals at the yarder or allow voice contact between the hooker and the yarding engineer.

Tame-ape: A husky individual who calls himself a logger and usually works on the rigging crews.

Tight-line: To pick logs up in the air and lower them down over rock bluffs into the saltchuck or to a lower landing where they can be loaded. It also means to hold the haulback tight enough to pick the butt rigging up out of the brush.

Tommy Moore block: A very wide sheaved block used when it is necessary to pull shackles or other small rigging through and over.

Tongs: Used to load logs.

Top Guy: Guyline uppermost on the spar tree.

Track Loader: Any log loader mounted on track undercarriage.

Tree Farm Licence (TFL): Gives the licensee the right to harvest a specified volume of timber which is supposed to result in sustained yield.

Turn: A number of logs being yarded in one trip.

Undercut: A large V cut in the front side of any tree to control the direction in which it should fall.

Underbuck: To cut a log from the bottom side up to prevent it from slabbing or splitting. When the old hand saws were used for bucking it was sometimes the only way to cut a log through.

Value-added: Obtaining additional value from a log over and above normal manufacturing, such as veneer, plywood or finger-jointed finishing materials.

Whistle Punk: See punk.

Widow-maker: A loose chunk of a limb or a tree hung up in another tree which can come down without warning and kill a logger.

Wire Axe: Usually an old axe used to cut cables when splicing has to be done out in the woods. Just lay the cable over the blade and a few blows with a sledge hammer will cut it cleanly.

Wolf Tree: An old rough tree with lots of limbs and rough bark.